The NEW ORDER of Man's History

JOHN COGAN

ELTON-WOLF PUBLISHING

Seattle • Los Angeles

The NEW ORDER of Man's History

Byron Corey!
Thank you for thelping my friend
Jeff Smith.
After you read the book give
me a call and we'll talk about it.
Good to be in touch
with you!

John Cogan
Feb. 2 '07

Cover design, David Marty
Text design, Paulette Eickman

02 03 04 05   2 3 4 5

ISBN: 1-58619-027-x
Library of Congress Catalog Card Number: 2001-088934

Second Printing September 2002
First Printing May 2001
Printed in Canada

Published by Elton-Wolf Publishing
Seattle, Washington

ELTON-WOLF PUBLISHING

2505 Second Avenue Suite 515   Seattle Washington 98121 (206) 748-0345
e-mail: info@elton-wolf.com   Internet: http://www.elton-wolf.com
Seattle • Los Angeles

To the late Giovanni Costigan, Professor of History at the University of Washington. An unsurpassed teacher of history, who imparted another quality to his instruction. He taught his students to think. He gave me my brain.

PREFACE

The purpose of this book is to trace man's evolution from ape-animal to ape-human and to correlate this development with the geophysical facts, such as the Ice Age, that caused the change. Man's journey begins in the trees of East Africa, moves to the savanna of North Africa, and then moves throughout the world of the tropics as he seeks to find a place to live in the diminished space of the Ice Age. Once man became bipedal and a hunter-gatherer, he quickly progressed mentally and physically to become the "modern man" of today.

The First Civilization developed to a high stone-age status, but it suffered greatly because of aridity caused by the Ice Age. North Africa became the Sahara desert and man had to leave and live elsewhere. He went east, north into Europe, and west to South and Central America. Just as man was successfully populating the world, disaster struck. An asteroid hit the earth in the North Atlantic Ocean (10,500 B.P.) causing the extinction of 70 percent of the megafauna of the world and almost destroying the Homo sapien populations. Man recovered and, after 5,000 years, four civilizations spontaneously appeared (Indus, Tigris-Euphrates, Nile, Central America). These civilizations mirrored the First Civilization and they resumed its evolutionary progress.

This history is based upon factual data taken from hundreds of sources available to all readers interested in anthropology, paleohistory, and geophysics. It is the interpretation of these facts that differentiates the New Order of man's history (as briefly described above) from the Old Order of man's history, the cornerstone of present-day academia, which holds that civilization began in the Mideast 5,000 years ago, and that the Americas were populated by Asians who (somehow) came south through the North American ice sheet.

Proudly, the New Order uses all available facts and evidence to support its case; shamefully the Old Order carefully picks and chooses certain facts to support its case, deliberately "ignoring" vast quantities of factual material that clearly disproves its assertions. The Old Order has the great advantage of being ensconced in academia from which it must be dislodged if the true history of man's past is to be known. Hopefully, this book will contribute to that end.

CONTENTS

Part I: The Ice Age

CHAPTER 1: THE BEGINNING

The universe is 15 billion years old. It began with an explosion, still in progress, called the "big bang" which was discovered by astronomer Edwin Hubble of the Mount Wilson Observatory, Los Angeles, California, in the 1920s. Hubble discovered through the massive telescope a "red shift" of the stars. Light observed from the stars when passed through a prism produced a spectrum (a range of colors) containing spectra (black lines evidencing the burning of chemical substances). These spectra "shift" toward the right or red side of the spectrum when the viewed object is moving away from the observer. Hubble found that the farther away a star is, the faster it is traveling (in direct proportion to its distance away) and the greater is the degree of the red shift. Thus, we can measure the extent of the primordial explosion by utilizing the red shift. By extrapolating the rate of expansion backward we arrive at the age of the universe, 15 billion years. And we also know the shape of the universe. It is an expanding sphere. From a given point on that sphere (earth) all cosmic matter is in fact moving away, as it would on the surface of an expanding balloon. The discovery of still extant lingering background radiation from the original explosion confirms the big bang theory. This discovery of 3 Kelvin universal blackbody (thermal) radiation occurred in 1965 at the Bell Telephone Laboratory at Crawford Hill, New Jersey. At first, the discoverers, Robert W. Wilson and Arno Allan Penzias, thought pigeon droppings caused the "humm" in a huge radio antenna. Later on, they realized what they had discovered. Aerial observations by U2 high altitude research planes confirmed that the radiation was uniform in all directions. The big bang theory was reconfirmed and expanded by a NASA project called Cosmic Background Explorer (COBE). The purpose of the project was to find if there was anisotropy in the cosmic background radiation. In other words, a slight variation in temperature in abutting "patches" of space. Only with anisotropy could the big bang theory stand, as anisotropy was required to differentiate light from matter and cause the formation of galaxies. A rocket into space carrying proper instruments, all to be designed and made would do the measuring job. After eighteen years of hard work by a scientific team led by John C. Mather, a United States Air Force Delta rocket took off from Vandenburg Air Force Base, California on November 17, 1989. The testing found anisotropy, perfectly confirming the big bang theory. Stephen Hawking referred to the discovery of anisotropy in the cosmic background radiation as "the greatest discovery of the century if not of all time."

Although the universe is 15 billion years old, our solar system is only 5 billion years old. We can prove the age of our system in a variety of ways such as measuring radioactive decay, analysis of earth rock, moon rock from the Apollo missions and analysis of fallen stony meteorites. Four to five million tons of meteorite dust fall to earth each year. In fact, we live in the remnants of a recycled star that exploded over 5 billion years ago, the detritus eventually coalescing into our Sun and solar system. Fred Whipple, an astronomer from Harvard and the Smithsonian, perhaps most clearly elucidated this theory of supernova explosion (many of which have been observed by man) followed by a nebula which eventually condensed into the Sun and planets. Note, however, how planetary existence comes into being: by the manifold collisions of the incipient planet with the countless particles, rocks, comets, meteors, asteroids, and miscellaneous debris of space. All of this matter gradually agglomerates to create the nine planet solar system as we know it. The process continues to this day.[1] The gentle word "coalesce" is in fact a poor mask for reality—a totally inept description of catastrophic impacts of stellar objects at astronomical speeds, which is the reality of planet building.

Thus, the earth began its spin and through evolutionary processes life began and progressed to the present day. For convenience, geologists have divided the history of the earth into divisions of time which divide at a point where there is a noticeable change in the fossils (once living organisms) found in sedimentary rocks. The greatest time period is the Precambrian, from the formation of the earth's crust 4.6 billion years ago to 570 million years ago. This is four-fifths of the time planet earth has been in existence, and during this time there was no life at all on earth. The subsequent periods are the Paleozoic ("ancient life") 570 million years ago to 225 million years ago; the Mesozoic ("middle life") 225 million years ago to 65 million years ago; and the Cenozoic ("modern life") 65 million years ago to the present. This latter unit is divided in part into the Quaternary period 2.5 million years ago to the present. In turn, the Quaternary is divided into the Pleistocene, 2.5 million years ago to 10,500 years ago (the Ice Ages); and the Holocene, 10,500 years ago to the present (after the Ice Age). The Quaternary is the time of man. His earliest apelike ancestors take an agonizingly long time, almost the entire Quaternary period, to develop into modern man. This transformation into Homo sapiens ("thinking man") occurred 150,000 years ago, late in the third Ice Age, in Africa.

A look at the geologic timescale discloses startling facts. First, for great blocks of time conditions on the earth remained the same. Earth revolved around the Sun, spinning on its axis, but each day was the same, for millions of years. The Mesozoic, or age of the dinosaurs, lasted 160 million years and the very existence of the dinosaurs bespeaks monotonous weather. The huge beasts were cold-blooded, warmed and kept alive only by the Sun. They reached gargantuan proportions such as the Brontosaurus, which weighed as much as 30 tons, was 70 feet long from head to tail, and had a brain the size of a walnut. Hence they existed in an almost somnambulant state, constantly eating to maintain enormous body mass. They could not cope with changing seasons, times of plenty and times of want, hot or cold weather, sun-rain-snow. In short, they lived in an absolutely different world than we live in today. Second, the geologic timescale shows us that our present epoch, the Holocene, is only 10,500 years old, a flyspeck of earth time representing only the time since the great ice sheets melted. All other time units are in millions of years. The Ice Age or Quaternary is 2.5 million years old and is subdivided into the Pleistocene lasting 2.49 million years when ice was extant; and the 10,500-year period of the Holocene, after the ice melted. Thus, we get the first clue to a most startling fact—that we live in a time of unusual and rapid geologic change unlike any other geologic period. There will be many further clues.

Our appreciation for the realities of geology and geological earth time is brand new and not at all highly developed. In 1830, Charles Lyell founder of modern geology stressed the ancient age of the earth and first explained that the processes that have shaped its features are the

GEOLOGICAL TIMESCALE

relative duration of eras	era	period	epoch	duration in millions of years (approx.)	millions of years ago (approx.)
Cenozoic	Cenozoic	Quaternary	Holocene	approx. last 10,000 years	
			Pleistocene	2.5	
Mesozoic		Tertiary	Pilocene	4.5	2.5
			Milocene	19	7
Paleozoic			Oligocene	12	26
			Eocene	16	38
			Paleocene	11	54
					65
	Mesozoic	Cretaceous		71	
					136
		Jurassic		54	
					190
		Triassic		35	225
	Paleozoic	Permian		55	
					280
		Carboniferous Pennsylvanian		45	
					325
		Carboniferous Mississippian		20	345
Precambrian		Devonian		50	
					395
		Silurian		35	
					430
		Ordovician		70	
					500
		Cambrian		70	
					570
		Precambrian		4,030	

formation of Earth's crust 4,600,000,000 years ago

same physical, chemical, and biological processes we see today. Or, in other words, very small annual changes applied over a great period of time. Unfortunately, this led academicians into the doctrine of uniformatism, precluding the possibility of any other cause (as an asteroid strike—something they knew nothing about then or now). Around 1910, the great German geophysicist Alfred Wegener developed the theory of continental drift. Time has validated this theory as the shape of the continents and the earth's stretch marks (crustal fracture lines) clearly show the movement of continents, just as mountain buildup proves the existence of tectonic pressure. Louis Agassiz deserves the majority of the credit for discovering the Ice Ages. In 1840, this Swiss-born Harvard professor published *Etudes sur les glaciers*. He concluded "great sheets of ice, resembling those now existing in Greenland, once covered all the countries in which unstriated gravel (boulder drift) is found." He was right, and 150 years later we have made considerable progress in analyzing the Quaternary—the Ice Ages. This work to date is only a beginning. There are countless scientific questions that need to be explored: what caused an Ice Age; what was Ice Age weather like; why did the Ice Age end so suddenly and violently; and how did the Ice Age affect man?

CHAPTER 2: THE FIRST ICE

The dinosaurs enjoyed 160 million years of warm and unvarying weather during the Mesozoic, 225 to 65 million years B.P. Then came their sudden and mysterious end. Next, the earth enters the golden age of mammals, which lasts for 63 million years during the Tertiary, 65 to 2.5 million years B.P. The climate remained stable during this time, cooling toward the end. Then the ice began its advance from the north in North America and Europe and from mountain strongholds around the globe. It had always been there, but it had not moved throughout the millions of years of the Tertiary. The advancing ice would profoundly affect the lithosphere, hydrosphere, atmosphere and biosphere of earth. It would be a direct cause of the civilization created by one of the plentiful mammals, Homo sapiens.

The ice advanced and retreated four times in the last 2.5 million years (the Quaternary).[2] We live in this world 10,500 years since the ice began its last retreat and still see all around us the effects of its recent presence: the ice-sculpted mountains of the Alps, Rockies, Southern Andes; the thousands of lakes in the northern and midwestern United States including the Great Lakes, lakes in Canada; and Puget Sound in Washington State. We must make a physical effort to remind ourselves how *recently* the ice covered North America, and what an incredible sight it was. A hypothetical office dweller in Seattle would see Puget Sound covered with 5,000 feet of ice. Hypothetical residents of Europe in Moscow, London, and Warsaw, as well as office workers in New York, Pittsburgh, Louisville, St. Louis, Omaha, and Great Falls would also see as much ice. For a time perspective we can compare the presence of ice at 10,500 B.P. in the low latitudes to some familiar landmarks. The pyramids were built 4,500 years before present, halfway to the time of ice. A bristlecone pine tree of the White Mountains of California is still alive at 4,500 years of age, again halfway to the time of ice. The permafrost that exists in the Arctic areas, and the very glaciers of the Rockies, Alps, and Greenland are remnants of the ice and permafrost that once covered one-third of the earth's land surface. The ice itself is over 10,500 years old.

The ice advanced at a rate between 200 to 400 feet per year. The last thrust of the ice continued for 117,000 years to 10,500 B.P. The date of maximum glaciation was 18,000 B.P. and after this date the ice began a cycle of withdrawal and advancement. At 10,500 B.P. the ice began to melt more rapidly, resulting in a withdrawal at the rate of .8 miles per year due to extensive climatic change, including significant warming of the atmosphere and oceans. For convenience we can say that the last glaciation took 117,000 years to build up and 4,000 years to melt. The precipitous melt began at 10,500 years ago and ended 6,500 years ago when the ice reached its present locations.

Ice moves because of the buildup of snow. More snow must fall in the winter than melts in the summer. The outward movement on the edge of a great ice sheet is caused by the pressure behind it. Most of that pressure comes from the center of the great sheet. North America's two great ice sheets were the Cordilleran, centered at approximately Juneau, Alaska and extending south to Seattle; and the Laurentide centered at Hudson Bay and extending south to New York City. Thus, cause (pressure) and effect (outward movement) may be thousands of miles apart.

The earth's atmospheric and hydrospheric currents comprise a complex system powered by the Sun. It is this system that creates glaciers and ice ages. Herein lies the unknown answer to the question: What caused the ice to move forward and then retreat? Scientists are not in agreement on the exact cause, but we can here enumerate the various factors. Some may be the cause of the beginning and end of an ice age. First, we must consider an apparent anomaly. To produce the snow, which created the glaciers, there must be the evaporation of seawater. This requires warm water not cold, which evaporates poorly. Air currents transport the water vapor over the glaciers; the water vapor condenses into snow as the temperature drops. Such a pattern existed for the 117,000 years of ice buildup. The Pacific Ocean fed the Cordilleran and Laurentide ice sheets and the Atlantic Ocean fed the European ice sheet. This general weather pattern still exists and, with a shock, we realize that glaciers do not require great cold. It would take only a drop of a few degrees in the world's temperature to start the ice moving again, just as it has done four times before in our present Ice Age. The atmospheric and oceanic temperature at the beginning of the last advance of ice were not radically different from today. At glacial maximum (18,000 B.P.) of course, it was considerably colder. Global temperature was 42°F then, and now it is 58°F (5.5°C to 14.4°C). What might make the earth cooler by six or seven degrees Celsius in the mid-northern and southern latitudes and start an ice age in the high latitudes?

Milutin Milankovitch has the answer. It rests in analyzing the spinning of the earth and its orbit around the Sun. A Serbian mathematical genius, he worked constantly from 1912 to 1941 to perfect his theory. Basically it states: there are three variables in the earth's cosmic existence, its axial tilt, its wobble about the axis, and its orbit around the Sun.[3] When the three variables coincide so as to produce the least solar heat to the earth between 55 degrees and 65 degrees latitude, the earth has an ice age. Ocean cores taken from the Indian Ocean in 1967 and the western Pacific and Indian Ocean in 1971, were analyzed by Nicholas Shackleton of Cambridge University and others. The result was the validation of the Milankovitch theory. Other factors influencing the advance or retreat of the ice sheets are mountain uplift and the Arctic Ocean. At low sea levels the ocean is more frozen, at high sea levels less frozen; the latter allowing it to be more of a source of precipitation.

CHAPTER 3: GLACIAL MAXIMUM

The great ice sheets of the world reached glacial maximum 18,000 years ago. In 117,000 years the ice in North America had advanced several thousand miles from its arctic source. Let us pause for a mental picture of its advance. The leading edge of the ice is usually high, a wall 500 to 1,000 feet high being pushed from behind and building up vertically because of friction with the ground beneath. Everything in front of it retreats, moves south. The rate of advance, 200 to 400 feet per year, is slow enough to create a glacial climate in front of the glacier, tundra for several hundred miles, a band of arctic willow and alder—at first dwarf size then larger, and a cold resistant forest of spruce. The ice displaced forests of pine and northern hardwoods. These forests moved south, displacing oak forests. Animals moved south ahead of the ice. In North America, the mountains run north and south; consequently, the animals survived—for a while. In Europe, the Pyrenees and Alps formed an east-west barrier (as did the oceans south of the British Isles). Many warm weather animals like the hippopotamus became extinct in these regions.

Certain statistics of glacial maximum will make a discussion of the earth's climate at that time more meaningful. Near the center of the sheets the ice was 10,000 feet thick, 500 to 1,000 feet at the leading edge, with an average thickness of 5,000 feet. The sheets contained 17 million cubic miles of ice, three times as much ice as exists in the world today. Ice and permafrost covered one-third of the earth's land surface. One-half the surface of the world's oceans were covered with pack ice, icebergs and floating ice. The storage of so much water as ice caused the seas to be 400 feet lower than today, forming land bridges around the world that do not exist today: the British Isles to the European continent, Malaya to Australia, and Siberia to Alaska. The drop in sea level exposed the sea bottom and continental shelves up to 250 miles, creating 10 to 15 percent more land area than the earth has today. The sheets pressed the land down, with a force of 250,000 pounds per square foot, to a measure of roughly one-third of their own height, as the earth's crust floats on a highly viscous but molten mantle. With the ice now gone, this earth is still rising today. Hudson Bay will eventually be dry. The great ice sheets created their own weather of unimaginable ferocity. This was caused by a temperature drop over the sheets, between its center and its edge, which produced an extreme temperature gradient, the formula for wind. Thus, the great ice sheets produced constant katabatic wind (cold air descending) frequently 100 miles per hour and often 200 miles per hour. These extreme velocities would be achieved as cold air masses 400 to 600 feet thick flowed like water over the ice, funneling into valleys. Atmospheric pressure caused an increase in speed, with the highest speeds occurring at the edge of the ice. In Wyoming, there is a geographical feature called "the fan of death" which is 150 miles deep and sculptured by glacial winds. When the wind blew over recently unglaciated land, it would produce monstrous dust storms, exceeding anything of today. Sand dunes in many parts of the world owe their existence to Pleistocene glaciers.

Some figures give us a sense of just how much colder the earth was during the Ice Age: At 18,000 B.P., the American Midwest averaged 18°F colder than now; Britain was 12°F (equal to present-day Alaska); the Atlantic Ocean water off the coast of Newfoundland was 26°F colder; and the mid-North Atlantic was 18°F colder than now.

All of this leads to one obvious fact: Nothing lived on or near the ice. Or, to state a corollary, every living thing that is now to be found in the once glaciated areas of North America, Europe, and elsewhere, is descended from ancestors that at glacial maximum lived in an ice-free area. The great sheets and surrounding terrain were as barren as the Moon, with no flora and no fauna.

Thus, the center of the North American continent was a cold, sandy, treeless, windswept desert at glacial maximum. All life existed in what is now the southern United States and on the West Coast north of the ice in Alaska. Eastern Siberia, and northern Alaska (together called Beringia) was unglaciated and largely treeless. It had a unique flora called the "Mammoth Steppe" because it was so suitable for the mixed diet required by the behemoths of grass, shrubs, and small trees. And it supported a great variety of large grazing mammals such as woolly mammoth, mastodon, musk ox, a species of camel, horse, bison (all extinct), and surviving mammals as elk, caribou, and Dall's sheep. These were preyed on by the short-faced bear, American lion, saber-toothed cat (all extinct), the surviving grizzly bear, wolf, and wolverine. Beringia was beset by raging arctic storms. There is evidence of vary sparse human population at a survival hunter-gatherer level going back from 35,000 to 20,000 B.P. when Siberia was first settled. For these struggling few, life was unbelievably hard. The Arctic Ocean seawater and North American Pacific Coast were extremely cold (from sea cores), and the land climate was truly arctic with fierce winds off the Cordilleran ice sheets. The climate was harsh but it was not a snow-ice-dominated habitat. It would be classified as cold-temperate. The grazing animals needed food of good quality and a lot of it. Today's tundra vegetation is decidedly poor quality for grazing. An adult woolly mammoth consumed 400 pounds of food per day; there were millions of woolly mammoths.

Now let us turn our attention to South America and Africa, both indirectly affected by the ice at maximum glaciation. All of South America east of the Andes was a magnificent savanna, including the Amazon Basin. It was the largest single landmass suitable for human habitation in the world. The tropical rain forest, which we are so familiar with, was restricted to a small area against the Andes in the very eastern portion of the Amazon Basin. Africa, which had once been a lush savanna, was at 18,000 B.P. a forbidding desert to 14°N latitude, almost to the equator (two-thirds of its landmass); only in the extreme south was it a savanna. The tropical rain forest was restricted to a small area in central Africa. The tropics in Africa and South America were much colder and drier than at present. Aridity, a phenomenon of the Ice Age, caused this and will also have enormous consequences in the history of that animal we will soon address: man.

CHAPTER 4: ARIDITY

The last interglacial period occurred before the beginning of the movement of the ice. We roughly date it from 130,000 to 117,000 B.P.[4] Thereafter the ice advanced slowly from 117,000 B.P. to glacial maximum at 18,000 B.P., began its melt, slowly at first, then with great momentum from 10,500 to 6500 B.P. Adding together the total time of the last interglacial and, arbitrarily, three-fourths of the time accorded to the advance of the ice, we have approximately 80,000 years of reasonably good weather for the temperate zone before the advent of the most serious adverse effects of the Ice Age on global temperature and tropical aridity. It was during this time that Homo sapiens made great progress from hunter-gatherer to civilization. The Sahara at the last interglacial was a wooded savanna filled with streams and lakes, that slowly dried up as the ice advanced. Between 60,000 and 18,000 B.P., conditions deteriorated, going from bad to worse. The Sahara became what it is today, the largest desert on earth. Its driest period was between 18,000 and 10,500 B.P. This was not only the time of the earth's coldest temperatures on land and oceans, but it was also the time of greatest aridity. We will list and examine the main factors that cause aridity, and deserts.

Through continental drift the continent of Africa moved northward into the tropical dry zone. A glance at a map shows a belt of deserts in these latitudes (Sahara, Arabian, Gobi, American Southwest). Nevertheless, the Sahara remained a very livable place for flora and fauna right up to the last thrust of the ice, as the geological record shows us. But the advancing ice triggered mechanisms of more immediate aridity. Atmospheric cooling at glacial maximum had greatly reduced the rate of evaporation from the open oceans, and there was no evaporation from the ice-covered sea (roughly one-half of the oceans); the colder winds carried less moisture. As a result there was a 20 percent decrease in worldwide precipitation on the average. The ice caused a worldwide increase in the velocity of the trade winds (those steady winds that blow east to west parallel to the equator caused by the turning of the earth on its axis) because the presence of the ice in the northern latitudes made for very low temperatures and contrasted greatly with the equatorial heat. This temperature gradation intensified the winds. The winds, in turn, intensified the ocean currents and produced greatly increased upwelling of cold ocean water. Strong winds combined with upwelling cold ocean water create the conditions for aridity. The Sahara is part of a worldwide pattern in this regard. All of the continents have upwelling cold water on their western shores. The water is especially cold between latitudes 35° and 15° in each hemisphere, which happens to be exactly off the Atlantic coast of the Sahara. Cold ocean water produces cold air and little moisture. Cold air is heavy and stays close to the ground, producing little rainfall.

Thus, the advancing ice served to create a great increase in the cold upwelling water off the west coast of the Sahara increasing the aridity in that area. But more important for the greater part of the Sahara landmass was the increased dryness and velocity of the east to west trade winds that cross the Sahara. Before the ice advance, the trade wind was farther south and carried moisture to the Sahara from the Indian Ocean and the Arabian Sea. The ice affected the jet stream which in turn moved the trade wind farther north where it collected much more dry air from the constant high pressure area of the 30° latitude. This is the Mideast of today—Saudi Arabia, Iraq, Iran, and Afghanistan. This arid county provided no moisture to the atmosphere that the winds could convey to the Sahara. Despite the melt of the ice, this weather pattern continues today.

As the sea is the source of moisture in the air, the distance inland and topographical features will affect precipitation. The Sahara landmass is immense, one-sixteenth of the land area of the world at the present time (as large as the United States), and at glacial maximum was even larger because sea level was 400 feet lower. Lack of rain produced the cold, dry, windy Sahara. Very slowly all the lakes and streams dried up, grass and trees disappeared, the animals left, and the terrain became the hard dirt and rock lunar landscape it is today. The Nile River was reduced in size to only 10 to 20 percent of its present flow.

The worldwide climate of the Ice Age produced dual phenomena. It covered one-third of the earth's land with ice and permafrost and another one-third of the earth's land with deserts (by creating the Sahara and exacerbating the others). The once lush Sahara succumbed to the constantly blowing, cold, dry east to west trade winds of high velocity and the cold, dry air of the North Atlantic Whorl (a clockwise circular movement of air over the North Atlantic Ocean). It became the world's most formidable desert because of the Ice Age. Where did the people living there go?

CHAPTER 5: THE MELT

The farthest thrust of the ice and its greatest volume was reached at glacial maximum 18,000 B.P. But at 18,000 B.P. the ice held, and then began a slow retreat with minor fluctuations of advance and retreat until 10,500 B.P. At that time the slow melt of the ice became rapid, amazingly fast, violating all of Lyell's slow and small change principles of geology. The ice was gone (that is, reduced to roughly its present position) by 6500 B.P. This incredibly fast melt remains unexplained and is one of the great mysteries of science. Later in this book reasons for the melt will be advanced.

The initial halt or retreat of the ice is explained by the Milankovitch cycles reinforced by the natural earth process of "starvation" and melting. Starvation occurred when snowfall became insufficient to supply the ice sheets. Here, the relation of the sea to the ice is all-important. Cold water produces little water vapor for evaporation; cold air holds little moisture; floating ice and pack ice preclude evaporation. The great size of the ice sheet made it difficult for moisture-bearing clouds to reach the center of the great sheets and starvation occurred. Interestingly, the great sheets built up over the millennia, not because of heavy precipitation, but rather because of lighter precipitation spread over thousands of years. As the ice began to melt from overall global warming, starvation continued to affect the ice sheets. The mass of freshwater from the great sheets froze readily, thinly covered great areas of ocean and blocked evaporation. Melting sea ice cooled the oceans in the summer, slowing evaporation. So the great sheets retreated from lack of supply of snow and melting from global warming. As we have seen the last advance of the ice took 117,000 years. The ice moved forward 200 to 400 feet per year but the retreat was precipitous, often up to .08 miles per year. In short order the great ice sheets were gone with most of the ice disappearing in the last 4,000 years from 10,500 to 6500 B.P. The great sheets did not merely melt from south to north as might be expected; they melted all around, from north to south, as well as south to north.

Let us try to form a mental picture of the retreating ice. As the ice melted its entire volume contracted. It did not melt just at the edge. Huge volumes of water were released. It flowed directly into the sea where glacier and sea conjoined or from the ice into streams and rivers, which flowed through the bare ground left by the retreating ice. The streams and rivers carried far more water than today, creating a terrifying landscape near the glacier of ice, rushing water and bare land. It will take hundreds of years to fill in behind the retreating glacier, but nature does. Willows, arctic plants, spruce, pine, and oak follow the ice and permafrost to the north. Animals follow the ice northward in both Europe and America, and man follows the animals.

The surfeit of water produced huge proglacial lakes (that is, formed in juxtaposition with a glacier). One authority states in part that, "... the aspect over much of Canada and other parts of the glaciated world would certainly be one that could be described as an island-studded freshwater sea." (James L. Dyson, *The World of Ice,* p. 241) Many of the proglacial lakes are now gone such as Lakes Agazziz and McConnell in Canada, and many remain such as Great Bear Lake and Great Slave Lake in Canada, and the Great Lakes in the United States. The history of glacial lakes is highly eventful. Colossal floods occurred. Now extinct lakes Columbia and Missoula in the Pacific Northwest (each the size of Lake Ontario) occasionally burst forth in a torrent when the ice dam broke (300 cubic miles of water!) and totally scoured southeast Washington State leaving the "Channeled Scablands" of the Columbia Plateau. The North American heartland and Finland are covered with lakes, formed by depressions caused by melted permafrost, glacial scouring, and the melting of isolated blocks of ice. Glaciers created Puget Sound in Washington State; Hudson Bay is a depression, caused by the center of the Laurentide ice sheet.

The land was also affected by the ice upon its retreat; we see the evidence of this everywhere. Moraines are piles of glacial drift, often gravel, that mark the edge or front of a glacier. Near Seattle, Washington the lobe of the Cordilleran ice sheet that created Puget Sound moved between the Olympic Mountains to the west and the Cascade Mountains to the east. In doing so, it deposited walls of gravel in the mountain valleys, mined now for local use and export, a valuable asset to the local economy. Erratic boulders (ice-transported rocks) are often seen in the once glaciated area, especially near mountains. A huge granite rock in the middle of loamy farm field is a sure sign of a Pleistocene glacier.

At glacial maximum, because of the water contained in the glacial ice, the worldwide sea level averaged 400 feet lower than it is at present. Then, in a very rapid fashion, the sea rose 400 feet worldwide because of the glacial meltwater. The rise began in earnest at 10,500 B.P. Present sea level was reached about 6500 B.P. The rising sea submerged over 10 percent of the earth's Ice Age land surface, eliminating the land bridges of the British Isles, Malaya, and Beringia. It covered continental shelves up to a very rough average of 150 miles, leaving undersea river canyons— the Hudson, for example. In the flat basin of the Caribbean, the sea covered the East Coast of Mexico at a rate of 200 feet per year. Rising water flowed over Beringia into the Arctic Ocean and created the Bering Strait. The entering Pacific water was warm, providing a strong clue as to why the ice sheets melted from north to south and all around. The Beringia climate changed from dry and intensely cold to a maritime climate, moister but still cold. This changed the flora and fauna. Tundra and boreal (northern) forest grew where before there was Mammoth Steppe. The great grazing animals suffered (mammoths, horses, bison), while others prospered (caribou). Toward the end of the melt when the Cordilleran and Laurentide sheets parted, the grizzly bear and moose made their way south to mid-continental North America.

The land recovered. Relieved of the burden of ice, it rose almost everywhere to some extent and markedly so in certain places. Of particular interest are the melt dynamics in Maine and Nova Scotia. A good part of Maine and Nova Scotia were under the sea at maximum glaciation because of the weight of ice. Here the land, rebounded (isostatic rise) now above the sea while farther south on the North American Atlantic coast, the encroaching sea inundated the continental shelf for as much as 250 miles (the eustatic rise of water level due to meltwater). In Greenland, the picture is more immediate. Since 12,000 B.P. the Greenland ice sheet margins have receded an average of 120 miles; and the land rose isostaticly toward the preglacial level, in some sections 400 feet. In Canada, one last great inland sea came into existence as the Laurentide ice sheet melted. It covered a great part of central Canada (two to three times the size of all the Great Lakes) reaching its greatest

size at 7000 B.P. But the land of central and east central Canada continues its isostatic rise, and the Tyrell Sea is now gone leaving as a remnant
Hudson Bay, which the still rising land will empty eventually. Man usually
experiences crustal adjustments due to isostaticly rising land as small-
scale, local earthquakes.

Thus, we see the melt of the great ice sheets in North America and
Europe as a time of change of great magnitude. The oceans physically
changed; the land physically changed; the climate changed. All of these
changes occurred very rapidly in a geologic sense, yet the process would
have been imperceptible to the vast majority of humans who now
inhabit the earth, as an individual man's life span is so short. But we
will see that intelligent man observed, lived through and recorded—
sometimes purposely, sometimes accidentally, directly and indirectly—
the presence of the ice and the consequences of its melt.

CHAPTER 6: THE ICE TODAY

The Ice Age (referring to the last glaciation only) was basically a phenomenon of the Northern Hemisphere. At glacial maximum it contained 97 percent of the world's ice. Antarctica, a continent of ice surrounded by open sea, did not change character, although during the Ice Age the weather was more severe than it is today. South America had increased mountain glaciers but only one in the Southern Andes that could be called an ice sheet. The melting ice reached its present size and location about 6500 B.P. For a convenient but very approximate measurement we can say it represents one-third of the volume of ice that existed at glacial maximum. Although its volume and extent has fluctuated since 6500 B.P., we may assume it has remained relatively constant to the present.

Glaciers now occupy 10 percent of the earth's surface and 97 percent of this amount is locked up in the great ice sheets covering Antarctica and Greenland, the rest in mountain glaciers. The Antarctic ice sheet is by far the larger being over six times the size of Greenland's. The Antarctic ice sheet only receives 6 inches of snow a year. In terms of water, this means it receives about as much as the hottest, driest Australian desert; yet the accumulated ice formed by the snow is 2 miles thick, therefore, very old. (It takes twenty years for fallen snow to become glacial ice). Antarctica is beset by constant and violent katabatic winds, often over 100 miles per hour. It is fiercely cold. There are no flora or fauna. The sea around it is constantly stormy. Thus, it has been and is now inaccessible to man and in fact is utterly uninhabited other than for maritime-oriented sea creatures.

The Greenland ice sheet is 1,600 miles long with a maximum width of 600 miles. Mountains rim the island and the interior is a flat plain. The ice varies from 3,000 feet thick to 2 miles thick, averaging 5,000 feet. Whereas the Antarctic ice goes right to the sea, around Greenland there is a land border varying from 12 to 120 miles wide interlaced with glaciers pouring ice into the sea. Greenland, like the Antarctic, is a desert with extremely cold temperature, high winds, and little precipitation. The climate is alleviated in its southwest corner due to the passage of the Gulf Stream far to the south. Otherwise, it remains fiercely cold and windy, with rapid weather change a hallmark. Some 47,000 people live on Greenland aided by modern technology to make life more bearable. Almost all are inhabitants of the far southwest corner with native Eskimos scattered elsewhere along the coast. All Greenlanders have one thing in common—none venture onto the glacial ice.

Permafrost, a first cousin to glacial ice, is more than frozen soil. It is underground ice mixed with dirt and it occupies 14 percent of the present dry land surface of the earth today (reduced from 20 percent at glacial maximum). Permafrost is often geographically associated with glaciers, at their margins, but it is in fact an entirely separate phenomenon. It depends strictly on subfreezing temperature for its existence. The permafrost belt extends all around the Arctic Ocean. Its narrowest zone is in Europe, because although Europe lies in a subarctic position at latitudes well north of the United States, it receives the benefit of the warm Gulf Stream. In Eurasia and Siberia, permafrost extends from the Arctic shore far south into Mongolia and Manchuria forming a single block of permafrost soil twice the size of the United States. Permafrost covers much of Alaska and one-half of Canada. Permafrost, just as the ice sheets of Greenland and Antarctic, is a living relic of the last glaciation because it is old, thousands of years old. It takes thousands of years to create permafrost. And it penetrates deep into the ground. At Port Barrow, Alaska and other places in Canada and Siberia it is known to be 1,000 feet deep or more, even up to twice that depth. The land surface of the permafrost area is covered with tundra in the north and the boreal forest in the south. As a rule, the winter snowfall is light in the permafrost area. In the summer, the snow will melt as well as a very shallow layer of the soil called the "active" layer, making human travel practically impossible. The underlying frozen soil prevents water from percolating and creates extensive swamps. Swamps breed mosquitoes; virtual clouds of them that can drive humans mad and kill young caribou (they cover the inner nasal passage and suffocate the animal). If the active layer is on a hill, it will slide; and if the hill has a boreal forest, the trees slide with the soil—giving rise to a "drunken forest." Permafrost heaves, moves, sinks, especially when a warm dwelling is placed over it.

In short, the polar regions and boreal forest today offer man little chance for occupancy. Although covering 20 percent of the earth's land, they contain only 2 percent of the world's population. Glacial ice offers absolutely no chance for habitation; the northern tundra, boreal forest, and muskeg offer virtually none. Even modern technology has made little difference, except to establish outposts for mining, oil drilling, and logging. The native people of this area struggle and survive only by great effort. It is somewhat surprising that most are recent arrivals who, for various reasons, migrated north. Asian tribal nomads migrated north to escape grassland droughts and attacking tribes. They found a life that was bearable but certainly no easier. In the whole Eurasian tundra there are approximately 30,000 tribal people who have a reindeer herding economy, moving north from the taiga (the boreal, northern spruce forest) in the summer to the tundra, then returning in winter. In North America Eskimos inhabit the Arctic Ocean shore and Greenland, numbering about 50,000 (Figures circa 1955). Until recently the Eskimos lived in a truly hunter-gatherer stone-age fashion. All of the peoples mentioned face annihilation from contact with modern western man. Ancient man in the Siberian-North American Arctic during the Ice Age fared no better, existing in small numbers and living under incredibly poor and harsh conditions, thousand of miles away from any sizable population base. Since the retreat of the ice, the polar lands and boreal forests have had the fewest modifications of any land areas on the earth.

The world oceans reached their present level at 6500 B.P. ago. The lifting meltwater came from the land ice sheets and the waterborne drift and pack ice that at glacial maximum covered one-half of the world's oceans but is now reduced to 7.3 percent coverage and is almost entirely confined to the polar seas. Icebergs, mainly from Greenland, still continue to be a serious menace to shipping. It is estimated that from 10 to 15,000 icebergs a year break loose from Greenland's glaciers. Some of these exceed a mile in length and rise 300 feet above the water. Many reach the North Atlantic shipping lanes, often enveloped in fog, and have caused shipping disasters, notably the sinking of the *Titanic* in 1912 and the *Hans Hedtoft* in 1959. The *Titanic* displaced 45,000 tons; the iceberg it hit displaced an estimated 200,000 tons. Thus, the ice and the oceans continue their symbiotic relationship; if all the ice on earth were to melt—

glaciers and permafrost—the oceans would rise another 200 feet.

Now, let us turn our attention to the present condition of two mid-earth areas that were affected by the northern ice at glacial maximum. These areas have particular significance for the history of man, the Sahara and South America. Although the great ice sheets are gone, the Sahara has not recovered. It remains the world's largest and most formidable desert. Its 3.5 million-square-mile area of today is about the same as at 18,000 B.P., the time of maximum glaciation, maximum aridity, and lowest temperature. It is huge, being one-sixteenth of the land area of the world. Rainfall "averages" 2 inches a year. The word "average" is very misleading as the rainfall is spotty, with great areas receiving no rain at all for years on end. Hot, dry winds constantly blow across the land by day, diminishing at night. The temperature does reach 130°F in the shade during the summer.[5] It is the hottest desert on earth with nine months of mean temperatures above 70°F. The weather is remarkably constant, like most weather in the trades. This is caused by subsiding air from a continental tropical air mass located to the northeast centered at 30° latitude and brought over the Sahara by the trade winds called the harmattan. The harmattan becomes hotter and dryer as it passes over the baking sand and rock. The air is dry, the sun hot, bright and relentless. A man must consume 10 pints of liquid a day to stay alive. The deadliest of all winds is the especially hot "sirocco" from the southeast. There is virtually no vegetation and dust is ubiquitous; the size of the sand grains dependent upon the velocity of the wind. There is a terrible incidence of eye disease. The causes of the failed recovery of the Sahara after the melt of the ice are many and not well understood. The ice had compressed weather patterns in the tropics causing severe aridity. The expansion of the weather patterns promised some relief, but it did not happen. The direction of relief would probably have been from the south, the Sudan, a transition zone of adequate rainfall. But it did not spread north, primarily because of a new influence on vegetation and the weather—man. The tropical woodlands and savannas, including the Sudan, cover 17 percent of the world's land areas and are occupied by 50 percent of the world's population. It is the consensus of experts in vegetation that the very existence of this habitat is due to fires set by man. Once these lands were far more forested, but primitive man would then set a fire in the dry season to aid in the hunt and/or to eliminate trees and provide more luxuriant grass for game. This was done all over the world; Africa being the prime example, the North American prairies a close second, and then interior Brazil. Next came overgrazing, especially by goats, and destructive farming. The Sahara is annually increasing in size toward the south rather than decreasing.

The Amazon Basin has changed considerably since glacial maximum. Equatorial winds bring much more rain now and large expanses of the once pleasant savanna and woodlands have changed into equatorial rain forest, an impassable jungle. Savanna remains in the Andes highlands and in the highlands north and south of the basin providing the type of landscape in which the vast majority of the continent's inhabitants live. In fact, the equatorial rain forest is decidedly unhealthy for humans. Tropical diseases abound and long residence in the extremely monotonous climate of heat and high humidity produces bad physiological effects on the human system. Tropical chills can occur and be fatal when the temperature changes only a few degrees if the body has lost its adaptive ability to adjust to temperature change, and the mind is enervated. The human beings who lived there when the climate was quite satisfactory, as at glacial maximum, moved to the more equable parts of South America as the climate changed for the worse.

Thus the Ice Age greatly affected two areas of the tropics that were of great importance to man: the Sahara and Amazon Basin. The Sahara was a magnificent human habitat until the middle of the Ice Age. Due to glacial aridity, the Sahara began an inexorable descent into the uninhabitable desert environment it became by glacial maximum and continues to be today. The Amazon Basin had an opposite experience. During the Ice Age it was an excellent human habitat, a semiarid savanna much like the former Sahara. But when the ice melted, increased rainfall caused it to become a tropical rain forest jungle, not fit for successful human habitation.

The ice has retreated, but are the Ice Ages at an end? No they are not. A long time will pass, the cold part of the cycle will return and the ice will again move south. But the present time is much more complicated than past probes of the ice where the time taken for the advance of the ice and the time taken for the retreat of the ice were equal. The precipitous melt of the great ice sheets has changed the rhythm of the Ice Ages. The last southward probe of the ice took 117,000 years to reach glacial maximum at 18,000 B.P. where it held until 10,500 B.P. The ice should have taken the same amount of time to retreat but, instead, a precipitous melt occurred between 10,500 B.P. and 6500 B.P., and the ice retreated to its interglacial position in only 4,000 years instead of the expected 117,000 years. Thus, the earth remains in the warming part of the cycle but without the cooling effect of the great, although shrinking, ice sheets. Much feared global warming can be expected for the remaining 100,000 years of the warm part of the cycle, then the cold part of the cycle will begin and the normal rhythm of the Ice Ages will be reestablished. Though the cosmos is responsible for 95 percent of the global warming, earth will suffer for man himself contributes atmospheric pollutants—"greenhouse gases"—which contribute to the effect. Undoubtedly, the tropics will be the worst affected, where 70 percent of the earth's bourgeoning human population lives, mostly in developing countries. This portends a very dangerous future for man.

Part II: Man out of Africa

CHAPTER 7: THE CT BOUNDARY

The earth's crust formed some 4.6 million years ago. Its exact state and composition we cannot know, but for 4 billion years the earth remained a lifeless orb going around the Sun endlessly—a microcosm in the universe, a speck of dust, unimportant, an absolute nothing in the cosmic scheme. Then, very belatedly, it changed. Life appeared. The first land plants and land animals appeared on planet earth somewhere around 435 million years ago and a long continuous saga to the present time began. On the geologic timescale this is in the mid-Paleozoic era ("ancient life" 570 to 225 million years B.P.), and the world was quite different.[6] The earth's land is thought to have been in one rather cohesive mass at the beginning of the era but then divided into two massive blocks as a result of continental drift and seafloor spreading. This initial separation has continued unabated to the present. The familiar continental land forms we now see when looking at a map are not those that existed in the Paleozoic era before the break up of the single landmass into continents. The present location of the landmasses of the earth was accomplished 26 million years ago, in large part. The Paleozoic era was followed by the Mesozoic era ("middle life" 225 to 65 million years B.P.).

The Mesozoic era has given modern man a wealth of mineral treasures: coals, salt, marine limestone and chalk, manganese, phosporites, iron ores, oil and gas, and many others. It was also a time of great volcanism with huge flood basalts occurring in Siberia, North Africa, southern Brazil, and India. The earth was uneasy with great granite mountain ranges rising throughout the world as in the western United States and eastern Asia. But surprisingly the global climate was more equable than it is today. There were no polar ice caps, and the same flora and fauna extended from the Arctic to the Antarctic. The world's temperature was obviously considerably warmer. Fossils of large reptiles and coral reefs have been found close to both poles; the presence of coal and iron ore deposits provide evidence of a more humid atmosphere.

Beyond this bare-bones description of known fact one is forced to speculate about the earth's condition. It appears there were no seasons in the Mesozoic era; each day was like the last, forever and ever as millions of years passed. Evolution of flora and fauna was slow but steady, not fueled by the struggle for existence forced by glaciers the size of continents, by drastic seasonal changes and ever-changing weather, all of which was to come later. We can describe such conditions of life as monotonous—exactly what was needed to produce animals that would become the most spectacular the earth has known: the dinosaurs.

These giant reptiles dominated the landscape. Some 440 different kinds have been identified; some swam, others flew, all walked, some ran, some roared and all laid eggs (many fossils of which exist). They were cold-blooded and needed the sun for bodily warmth. The Brontosaurus was 30 tons in weight, and usually supported itself in water, yet it had a brain the size of a walnut. It was far too stupid to contend with today's climate; it could never plan ahead for winter; it could never learn a range of territory; with such a pittance of a brain, it is remarkable that it could even reproduce. Every waking moment of its entire life was spent eating. Its conditions of life were necessarily remarkably stable. The great predator Tyrannosaurus Rex weighed 5 to 10 tons (its bones alone were 2 tons) and was 40 feet long and 20 feet high; Tyrannosaurus Rex was fast. A running step by the monster was 9 feet in length. Its body acted as a huge teeter-totter with the large rear legs as a fulcrum balancing the massive head and neck to the fore and its huge tail to the aft. The world contained hundreds of millions of these magnificent dinosaurs; yet at the end of the Cretaceous period (the last period of the Mesozoic era) about 65 million years ago, they vanished from the face of the earth along with many other fauna and sea life in a sudden extinction of overwhelming proportions. The cause of which is said to be a mystery, but recent scientific thought leads to a straightforward answer. An asteroid hit the earth at that time.

Earth still enjoys the presence of some relatives of the dinosaurs, however. Alligators, turtles, lizards, and snakes had direct ancestors alive at the time of the dinosaurs. Birds are more directly related, their feathers being highly modified scales of a reptile's skin. Many fish that exist today were alive at the time of the dinosaurs. The sturgeon exists in most of the great rivers of the world. Unmolested, they can grow to over 1,000 pounds and great old age. The sturgeon's physical structure is ancient; its body is supported by cartilage instead of bone. The coelacanth is simply unbelievable. Probably 350 million years old, it was believed to have become extinct 60 million years ago. To the astonishment of scientists, a live specimen was caught off the southeast coast of Africa in 1938; another was caught in 1952. Since then underwater photographs have been taken of these huge metallic-blue, predatory fish, with fins that are in fact rudimentary legs, vivid reminders that all life came from the sea.

After the Mesozoic era the geologic timescale moves to the third and last era of geologic time, the Cenozoic era ("modern life" 65 million years B.P. to present). The last geological period of the Mesozoic era is called the Cretaceous (136 to 65 million B.P.), and the first geological period of the Cenozoic is called the Tertiary (65 to 2.5 million B.P.). Because of the great extinction of land and sea life that occurred 65 million years ago there is frequent reference to this time as the "CT boundary."

Attention now focuses on another group of fauna that existed late in the age of dinosaurs and somehow managed to survive the great extinction at the CT boundary: the mammals. Derived from reptiles, mammals originate as an evolutionary strain at the beginning of the Mesozoic era, 225 million years ago. For millions of years certain fauna existed that had characteristics of both reptile and mammal, but as eons passed the differentiation became complete. Even now a precise definition of either group is impossible because of fringe species such as the platypus, aardvark, and whales. The marsupials, with a pouch for young (kangaroo) are extremely primitive mammals dating directly back to the early Mesozoic era. In general, mammals are said to be backboned animals, the young nourished by its mother's milk, are warm-blooded, four-limbed and usually have hair. Approximately 4,000 species of mammals now exist exhibiting a great diversity of form and life adaptation from a small mouse to a colossal whale. The earliest mammals were very small, active, predators, and terrestrial (earthbound habitat). As the eons passed, some learned to burrow in the ground, others to fly, some returned to the sea (whales) and some adapted to an arboreal habitat. This last group will lead us to man.

CHAPTER 8: MAN APPEARS

From the CT boundary to the present the 65 million years of the Cenozoic era is termed the Age of Mammals, just as the previous 165 million years of the Mesozoic era is termed the Age of Reptiles. Now it is the turn of the mammals to dominate the earth. From their humble beginnings at the start of the Cenozoic era, some rodentlike animals would increase hugely in size (elephants, mammoths) and all would become specialized (moles, giraffes, beavers, squirrels). Only one order, the primates, would develop into a unique species with a totally generalized body and the largest brain. Man is indeed nature's experiment in the enlarged brain, just as the giraffe is nature's experiment in a long neck. The development of a single organ to preeminence is totally in accord with Darwinian evolution. With all plant and animal life multiplying at a geometric rate and the food supply only at an arithmetical rate per Malthusian law, each animal seeks to find its niche in the economy of nature, that is, an existence where it will find the least possible competition. The often-cited "struggle for existence" and "survival of the fittest" are true enough statements but are corollaries to the rule of specialization rather than representing the main thrust of Darwin's theory. Thus, man's history on planet Earth is nothing more than a study of one case of animal evolutionary specialization.

The study of man's anthropologic history is a young science, and its findings are quite incomplete due to the imperfect and incomplete archaeological record. Modern anthropology dates from 1859 with the publication of Charles Darwin's sober and masterful tome, *Origin of Species*. It instantly became clear to any thinking individual (and there were few in religiously saturated Victorian England) that man was an animal, and therefore, like all animals was a product of evolution.[7] Darwin suggested that Africa would be the most likely place to look for man's ancestors, as it was inhabited by two of man's closest relatives, the gorilla and the chimpanzee. Darwin's hunch was valid, and after years of work by anthropologists there now exists a working framework of fossils detailing man's history from his primate past to his anthropoid present.

We know there are thousands of mammal species, and we know that many thousands of these species are now extinct. In fact 99.9 percent of all species that ever existed are now extinct. Inevitable extinction seems to be a rule of nature. Its causes are complex in some cases and rather obvious in others. Inability to compete, overspecialization, predation, disease, change in conditions of life, such as habitat and climate, are all factors. Some scientists purport to detect certain rhythms in patterns of extinction; they maintain that a species has a certain life expectancy (about four million years), and no species goes on forever. Thus, from the beginning of the age of mammals 65 million years ago to the present time, although we track man's development from a low mammal to a primate to an anthropoid ape to Homo sapiens, we must never forget that there were many branches of the family tree. Many species of primates and apes that very closely resembled the species that would become man succumbed to extinction. This time journey then is one from lower animal to higher animal with brain specialization serving as a measure of progress.

Man's ancestors developed in the tropics because the cold of the Ice Ages made existence impossible in the north for animals not totally cold-adapted. As Richard Leakey points out, Africa of 15 million years ago was forest from east to west and supported a great population of diverse primates and many various species of monkeys and apes. By 12 million years ago tectonic forces had greatly changed Africa and created the Great Rift Valley, which approximately bisects Africa, north to south. West Africa became jungle, humid, arboreal. East Africa became a land of great contrasts with hot, arid lowlands and cool, forested highlands. This set the scene for the rapid evolutionary advance of the tree-dwelling apes of East Africa. Life in the trees greatly aided these apes. Prehensile hands and feet developed. With such extremities, tools could be made and useful work accomplished. Eyesight was highly developed. It takes excellent three-dimensional vision to swing through trees. And a light, lithe body could become adapted to many uses and many climates. Being generalized in form (no fangs, claws, hairy coat), only the brain could help the ape if it descended from the trees and joined the other animals on the ground in the struggle for survival. All scholars agree that upon its descent to the ground the African protohuman-ape began an evolutionary development in an order: first gait, then body, then brain.[8]

There is a great deal of argument over what makes an ape "human." That is, what are the characteristic traits that differentiate an ape from Homo sapiens—the ape-human of today? For Richard Leakey it is bipedalism, a physical trait of such importance that it alone defines a human, and other scholars join him. Bipedalism gave freedom to the hands, which led to tools and thinking as a way of life. Ancestral apes—as exemplified by the fossil-find Procounsul that existed 16 million years ago—lived in the trees, walked on all fours, were probably tailless and lived on fruit.[9]

Around 7 million years ago in East Africa some species of formerly tree-dwelling apes became bipedal and ground-dwelling, the first proto-humans. Species of primitive apes varied in size from chimpanzee to gorilla. Thus, it can be said that the physical characteristics of primitive apes led to one of their species eventually becoming human. We can clearly see this today. There are five anthropoid apes, Homo sapiens, gorilla, orangutan, gibbon, and chimpanzee (which is 97 percent genetically human). Man's body came first with upright posture, eyes with color vision and depth perception, and a prehensile hand. His brain developed later, goaded on by his physical development and responses to the environment. This last development of the ape-human, the enlarged brain, is what finally differentiated the other four anthropoid apes from Homo sapiens. But even for today's Homo sapiens, the transition between the animal-ape and the ape-human is still in play both physically and mentally.

Darwin and countless other researchers into the working of the human mind have no difficulty in identifying various human instincts that are animal, primordial, and universal: self-preservation, sexuality, aggressiveness, pleasure, communal, family, and others. Certain of these instincts are in fact magnified by an anthroponomical phenomenon, the fact that it takes so long to raise a human child to independent adulthood. Hence, the necessity of family for child-rearing; they also required a group or small community for hunter gathering and mutual protection. All of which serves to put the brain to work; that is, to think ahead, to plan, to communicate, to agree, disagree, and compromise. We now realize that modern man (Homo sapiens) has only possessed his large brain for 150,000 years; his linkage with the anthropoid apes is massive and with the chimpanzee, overwhelming. Modern research holds that Homo sapiens diverged from the gorilla-chimpanzee lineage from 5 to 7 million years ago. Their skeleton differs from men only in degree: the number of cranial bones and teeth are the same, hands and feet are remarkably similar. It has been determined that humans and chimpanzees have 99 percent of their DNA in common, the essence of heredity. It might as well be said that anatomically and genetically humans and chimps are 1 percent different. In fact the only distinguishing characteristic is the size of the brain. A gorilla's brain ranges from 450 to 600cc, the chimpanzee's from 300 to 485cc, and Homo sapiens' from 1,100 to 1,500cc. But as one goes back in time, man's brain size diminishes until it is apelike and probably no bigger than other competing anthropoids. Thus, man carries his animal ancestry in his bones and genes; he also carries it in the workings of his brain.

In a book reduced to obscurity by disapproving academic pundits, *The Expression of the Emotions in Man and Animals*, Darwin thoroughly analyzed the uniformity of expression used by animals and man to instinctively express certain emotions: baring one's teeth in anger, wide-eyed fear, threatening postures, obsequious gestures like rolling over, kneeling or bowing, and many others. Fortunately, there is a rebirth of interest in the book as modern academics rediscover its obvious truth: that man's emotions as evidenced by his expressions and visceral reactions are purely animal.

As the bipedal ape progressed, the "wiring" of its brain changed. In the lower animals the brain is the focus of the nerves of the body almost solely for the purpose of motor skills with little space left for cognitive thinking. As man's ancestors progressed this wiring changed to make more cortical brain area available for cognitive thinking and less area for muscular motor skills. Thus, the size of the human brain and its wiring are factors that differentiate Homo sapiens from the lower animals—nothing else.

The anatomy of the human brain shows its progress from primitiveness to its modern form. During gestation, the human embryo passes through the full evolutionary history of the human race. At about four weeks the fetus has gills that later close, forming the human head. From the fifth to seventh week the fetus has a tail which extends remarkably far between the legs. This tail later atrophies and becomes the coccyx or tailbone. (For up to six weeks it takes an expert to distinguish between a human, a chicken, or a frog embryo).

Think of the brain as nothing more than a bulb on the end of a stem, and that man is physically very much like a tadpole: the human backbone is the stem (from which four appendages dangle—arms and legs) and the brain is the bulb on its end which is divided into three parts as is described by Carl Sagan in *The Dragons of Eden*. The first and most primitive part is the brain stem, its reptile heritage known as the R-complex, seat of aggressive instincts, territoriality, ritual and social stratification, all very animalistic—the downside of human nature. The second part is the Limbic System, the brain's mammalian heritage, seat of emotions (reptiles apparently had almost none), smell (an adjunct to memory), and memory. The third part, the Neocortex is especially human, the site of cognitive functions such as very long-term memory, planning for the future, activities such as mathematics, science, technology, music, art, and even our upright posture itself which led directly to modern man. Thus, the brain, a 3-pound piece of meat, is an organ that has been subjected to evolutionary development and shows it in its structure and in its functions. Sagan puts it succinctly: "My fundamental premise about the brain is that its workings—what we sometimes call "mind"—are a consequence of its anatomy and physiology and nothing more."[10]

CHAPTER 9: EARLY MAN

The East African bipedal ape has left the trees, and its habitat is now the ground. The long journey to humanness has begun. Perhaps Lucy best exemplifies the paleoanthropological time point of three million years before present. Professor Donald Johanson found Lucy's bones (pieces of skull, arm bones, pelvis, thighbone, and ribs) in the Afar area of Ethiopia on November 30, 1974. The find was immensely significant because it was, at the time, the oldest hominid found (three million years old) and the most complete skeleton. Lucy was a full-grown young female, slightly larger than a chimpanzee (3 feet, 7 inches) about the size equivalent of a six-year-old child. Her curved fingers and toe bones show her tree-climbing heritage, but her pelvis and leg bones show bipedalism —again, at the time, the oldest confirmed bipedalism of an ape. Her brain was small and apelike at 500cc and her jaw was apelike, but she was definitely hominid. We thus have a good mental picture of one of our earliest ancestors. One well suited to the appellation, "the missing link."

Now we must allow for time and space. Northern Africa, the Sahara, composes 16 percent of the land area of the earth. Add East Africa and it approximates 25 percent. At Lucy's time and for several million years thereafter this area was quite well suited to the lifestyle of Lucy's kin. It is quite fair to imagine hundreds of thousands of hominid apes occupying this area at any one time. Thus, the stage is set for marked evolutionary progress and the fossil record proves this occurred.

We now take a quantum leap in time to 1.6 million years before present and examine Turkana boy found by Richard Leakey and Alan Walker on the shore of Lake Turkana, Kenya on August 13, 1984. This was an exceptional find as the skeleton was quite nearly complete, a great rarity when not associated with a burial. Found in the Okote Tuff strata, the fossil was dated easily at 1.6 million years. Turkana boy was twelve years old, but a shocking 5 feet, 6 inches in height! (Adults would be 6 feet tall or more.) The skull is distinctly human and apelike features are greatly modified; it had a human jaw rather than the powerful jaw of an ape; the teeth were smaller; it had a human chin—formed to chew on one side rather than gnaw like an ape; the Broca's area and Wernicke's area of the skull case prove it had meaningful speech. The long femur bones show a fully erect bipedal gait and because of a narrow pelvis (more narrow than modern man's), it actually was superior to our present bipedal gait! Anthropologists believe that the human pelvis widened after Turkana boy's time to allow the birth of a fetus with a larger brain. Turkana boy is classed as a pioneer member of Homo erectus ("erect man"), a true human being in all regards, with a brain capacity of 750cc early on—increasing to 1,325cc later on (as opposed to a modern human's 1,500cc). Homo erectus was immensely successful. His population rose to massive numbers, and he spread over all of Africa and Eurasia by 350,000 B.P. There is a clear continuity of evolutionary progress, cultural and technical development through Homo erectus' time until the progress is so great that we identify the species as Homo sapiens ("thinking man") about 150,000 years ago.

Homo erectus' journey to modern man was programmed in his mental and physical structure, which reacted to the environment and climate in which he lived. The mild forests and savannas of East Africa and North Africa teemed with animals and led this earliest man to change from former forest-living habits to that of an open plain hunter-gatherer— the most momentous single event in all of human evolution. Homo erectus had excellent eyes for hunting as a result of millions of years in the trees. Capable of near and far vision, they saw in full color (many animals see only black and white) and had excellent depth perception. His bipedal gait freed his hands for the use of tools and weapons; a nomadic life produced the lithe body; the hunting and gathering way of life led to cognitive thinking—to produce tools and to plan ahead as to matters of living and hunting, which in turn required social organization. And by being a hunter-gatherer he became geographically free. The other anthropoid apes are fruit-eaters and confined to the tropics, but a meat-eater has all the animal resources of the cold zone at his disposal. Hunting required Homo erectus to outthink his prey, which required an analysis of its habits, and called upon intelligence, courage and skill in its capture, including the social skills of leadership and cooperation. Gathering required acute powers of observation, a "mind's eye" of special geographic memory, and a respect for the changing seasons in the colder climates, man's first extraterrestrial awareness. Hunting and gathering proved a very successful way of life for Homo erectus. The eating of meat as opposed to a strictly vegetarian diet gave him more leisure, a basic necessity to advance toward his unknown goal—civilization.

If one quality is above others in evolutionary importance arising out of man's hunter-gatherer lifestyle it is the premium placed on intelligence. Man was forced to develop cognitive thinking to survive. That is, he had to learn from the teaching of his peers, experience, remember what he had learned, and have the imagination to apply that knowledge to different situations in the future. It is no surprise, therefore, that over 1.5 million years the brain of Homo erectus grew from 750cc to 1,325cc or more by 150,000 B.P. Homo erectus was a very intelligent human being.

The first stone tools appear in Africa about two million years ago. They are a good measure for the beginning of the hunter-gatherer phase of man's evolution. From that time on there is a continuous progression of complexity in the human line. During this early period, man ate raw meat and was a cannibal.[11] The first real evidence of a cooking fire was found near Marseille, France in the Eseale cave, estimated at 750,000 years B.P. Man's developmental curve appears flat at first, rising toward the end, markedly so after the advent of the use of fire. However, we must be very careful about dating the first use of fire. The climatic change that caused the creation of the Sahara desert effectively wiped out the archeological record of many of man's early achievements. Man undoubtedly used fire well over one million years ago in North Africa. During the time of the development of Homo erectus (2 million to 150,000 B.P.) Africa, north and east, was bountiful. The African landscape was a savanna, a plain mixed with trees and mild forest. The Sahara had many rivers and lakes ideal for humans, and the teeming animals provided plentiful food. But hunting bands require a certain amount of territory and population pressure increased. Homo erectus moved out of Africa toward the east. By 700,000 B.P. they are found in China and Southeast Asia. How they accomplished this journey remains a total mystery. Hunting bands were fiercely territorial and greatly resisted any impetus to move. There was absolutely no concept of travel for adventure. Moreover, the population pressure must have been severe, providing the only explanation for this emigration.

Homo erectus moved through Eurasia below a line of latitude that marked the cold zone with one exception, Neanderthal man, who lived north of this line in Europe. This imaginary line of the cold zone would not be crossed until Homo erectus had advanced evolutionarily to Homo sapiens, modern man, who at last would be ready to deal with the cold. The one exception to this rule—Neanderthal man—ventured into an area north of the Mediterranean and south of the great ice-age glaciers of Europe and as far east as modern-day Israel. Neanderthal man was named after the south German mountain valley where the first remains were found in 1855. Neanderthal man inhabited this area from 200,000 to 20,000 B.P., overlapping with Homo sapiens the last 10,000 years. Then the Neanderthals disappeared utterly, completely, without further trace. The race is an enigma and of great interest to science since it represents a unique variation of Homo erectus raising all the questions of how did it come to be, why did he live in this part of the world, why did he fail? We have some facts at hand, and must speculate as to others. The major part of the range of Neanderthal man was directly south of the European ice cap. He lived there long enough to go through one inter-glacial period before the ice advanced for the fourth and last time, but we know very little about this time and the archeological record only details his life during the last Ice Age (which lasted from 117,000 to 10,500 B.P.). The weather was extremely cold with very short, cool summers reaching 70°F and with six-monthlong winters and temperatures averaging 20°F below zero, with heavy snows. Dry spells occurred making it possible to hunt. The cold preserved meat, and there was a lot of meat—woolly mammoth, reindeer, horse, ox, deer, rhinoceros, and small game. Neanderthal man's physique was a perfect adaptation to cold weather conditions. He was short (not over 5 feet, 4 inches) and massive (huge trunk, limbs, bones); he had a brain averaging 1,450cc (equal to modern man's although certainly "wired" more to the muscles). His head was primitive with massive brow ridges, low forehead, heavy upper jaw, nearly chinless lower jaw, and a pronounced "snoutiness" around the nose. Powerful muscles made him incredibly strong, and he needed this strength for heavy loads and for using the stone spears with which he killed big game. He lived in caves and in the Ukraine in huts (made of mammoth bones). His society was the hunting band, and he had a modicum of culture that included formal burial rituals. However, he had no art and left no other artifacts that would demonstrate cognitive thinking beyond that which was necessary for survival. And, in fact, this is what doomed Neanderthal man—his brain failed him. It seems to have ossified, and his stone tools of 150,000 B.P. are the same as those of 40,000 B.P., as is his whole way of life. This prolonged stultification of progress is unique to Neanderthal man and science has no idea why it happened. Because of these factors, he was no match for a new arrival in his world: Homo sapiens, modern man.

CHAPTER 10: MODERN MAN

We have to be amazed at Homo erectus. He is observed steadily changing, his brain growing, his physique improving from the time of Turkana boy at 1.6 million to 150,000 B.P. at which time the change is so great that we give him another name: Homo sapiens sapiens ("thinking man"), who is usually referred to simply as Homo sapiens. If we could magically bring to life a number of Homo sapiens who lived 150,000 B.P., give them clothes, education and a normal upbringing; they would have no trouble at all fitting into the society of today. They would look, act, and think like everyone else and could easily hold any job from bus driver to atomic scientist. When we study "primitive man" of 150,000 years ago, let's get it straight: we are studying ourselves.

If we compare Homo sapiens to Homo erectus there are noticeable physical differences. The average Homo sapiens' brain size is larger at 1,500cc, compared to 1,000cc for Homo erectus; Homo erectus has more fanglike (apelike) canine teeth; erectus has a poorly developed chin; erectus has a pronounced single brow ridge rather than two separate brow ridges. In general Homo sapiens is more gracile in the face, taller and more lithe of body. But now for the surprise. If we switch our comparison to Homo sapiens of 150,000 years ago and modern man of the Middle Ages there is a massive physical difference! A number of skeletons of Homo sapiens found in Europe (well over 200) dating from 40,000 to 10,500 B.P. (Cro-Magnon man) show a remarkable individual 6 feet, 2 inches to 6 feet, 5 inches (or more) in height with a brain from 1,600 to 1,800cc in size with a well-formed head indicating that the "wiring" of the brain emphasized cognitive thinking rather than muscle control. Modern man of the Middle Ages averaged 5 feet, 2 inches in height, with an average brain size of 1,500cc wired for cognitive thinking, but overall, not anywhere near the specimen in brain size and physical stature of earlier Homo sapiens. Homo sapiens diminished greatly in stature and brain size everywhere in the world around 10,500 B.P., and only now is regaining his lost physical size and brain capacity. Curiously 10,500 B.P. is exactly the time a great number of species of the large animals of the world went extinct swiftly and suddenly. There is an obvious connection here, which we will explore later.

The mental processes of Homo sapiens were the same in the beginning as they are now. The first thing to disabuse ourselves of is any thought that primitive man was childlike. Nothing could be further from the truth. As Franz Boas, Paul Radin, and many other outstanding anthropologists attest: "there is no fundamental difference in the ways of thinking of primitive and civilized man . . . the mental processes among primitives and civilized are essentially the same . . . civilized man has (not) attained a higher place in mental organization than primitive man." (Franz Boas, *The Mind of Primitive Man.*) In clinical fashion Boas illustrates the point by examples: primitive man inhibits his impulses, has great power of attention, uses logical thinking and has great originality. As a caveat, he states: "The effect of civilization upon the mind has been much over estimated." One example of this is how emotion influences human conduct. Both primitive and civilized man have found it difficult to apply reason over emotion. In *Primitive Man as a Philosopher* and *Primitive Religion,* Paul Radin holds that there is an identical distribution of ability and temperament in primitive and civilized societies. Primitive societies had thinkers, leaders and an intellectual class. In fact, whereas primitive man viewed life with equanimity, modern man faced with the truth about human nature, and his insignificance in the cosmos drops into despair and religion for escape.

There is no difference in the cultures of primitive and modern man. The impetus to cultural expression was and is the same although its mode of expression is different. Our animal heritage is the touchstone of human culture. The anthropoid apes are a part of the social primates that exist, to varying degrees, as integrated groups of animals. The apes have keen eyes and prehensile hands and feet; and, in the case of Homo sapiens, there is the enlarged brain. These attributes are the requisite tools for culture. Culture can be called the environment that man creates for himself. It is composed of concrete things such as clothing, buildings, airplanes and abstract concepts such as entertainment and philosophy. It is above and apart from nature. Man only arrives at a high cultural level after a long evolutionary journey of body and mind. Another requirement is a huge population, duly organized. Thus, culture's end product is civilization—whether ancient or modern—but its source is the mindset of a social animal, which has the proper physical tools of body and brain.

Hence we now see the bipedal East African ape in a new light; evolution has brought him to Homo sapiens, modern man, about 150,000 years ago, and he is fully ready to dominate the world stage. He has physical ability (physique), mental ability (brain size and wiring), which by 40,000 B.P. is superior to modern man's, and the requisite social organizing ability (innate to primates and complemented by the hunter-gatherer lifestyle). Now he will face challenges from the environment in the form of the ice, cold, and aridity of the Ice Age, as well as his own circumstances, overpopulation. Homo sapiens will begin the struggle to improve himself in order to survive, and we begin to see the first glimmerings of "history" as we track his progress.[12]

Modern man is often referred to as a product of the Ice Age. Homo erectus, his predecessor, had developed over approximately two million years in Africa, during which time the northern ice made several advances and retreats, changing the weather, the climate, and the environment of north and east Africa. Over time, Homo erectus spread throughout the tropical Eurasian world, driven by overpopulation which was periodically exacerbated by adverse living conditions. Homo sapiens at 40,000 B.P. presents an uncannily similar experience to Homo erectus' prior experience in his need to move about the earth in order to find living space.

The first Homo sapiens skeletons are found in Africa and date to about 150,000 B.P. The skeletons found in the Near East and Far East are later dating, from 100,000 to 80,000 B.P. This leads the great majority of anthropologists to believe that Homo sapiens originated in Africa and then spread out. We know he moved about because he entered Australia and its environs around 50,000 B.P.; he entered the Neanderthal homeland (Europe south of the glaciations) around 40,000 B.P. Later, about 20,000 B.P., he enters the New World where no Homo sapiens had ever been before. This clear pattern of worldwide movement seems to most strongly support an African origin for Homo sapiens. As the distances covered are large (the entire tropical belt) the population source fueling the spread must have been massive. When we then reflect on where could such a massive population live, we see the obvious—North Africa, now the Sahara desert, which was man's original homeland and has been his homeland all along. It is one-sixteenth of the world's landmass and could hold a population of millions of hunter-gatherers. With agriculture, the area could sustain many millions of people. In fact the degree of cultural development can be a measure of the amount of human population. Hunter-gatherer peoples are sparsely settled, basic agriculture intermediate, and high-cultural achievement (marked by monumental construction) indicates a very large population. There can be overpopulation leading to emigration at any step of cultural development, as Homo erectus and Homo sapiens both prove.

Part III: The First Civilization

CHAPTER 11: MODERN MAN AND THE ICE AGE

The very movement of man about the vast unknown reaches of the world is a clear signal that a new era in Homo sapiens' history has arrived. This movement is intelligent, directed, focused. And we know that Homo sapiens of 150,000 B.P. ago had superior physical prowess and a greater brain size than our own. Thus, the stage is set for this particular anthropoid ape to make a great advance, from hunter-gatherer to a true civilization. It is a change both in thinking and lifestyle. Whereas hunter gathering took place in a natural environment, civilization is an artificial environment—a human creation. It is an expression of cognitive thinking, of abstract thought practically applied for the purposes of obtaining a more comfortable, pleasant and secure living, but often sadly enough drifting off into destructive religious fantasies (as are highly visible today). An incipient civilization always begins on a river. People must have water for personal use, for domesticated animals, for crops, and for transporting people and goods. We want to take important notice of this point: early man's full appreciation of the advantages of water transport. It is the singular key to his first civilization. In fact, some anthropologists muse that man's first tool was not a stone flake but a few logs made into a raft.

Man's First Civilization began in the area of greatest population density, North Africa in the part that is now the Sahara desert. This First Civilization expanded greatly from there, as we shall see. In fact it spread worldwide. Not much hard archeological evidence of this First Civilization exists today because it was destroyed by an asteroid impact of incalculable violence that came very close to exterminating Homo sapiens from the earth. (Many species of megafauna were exterminated.) This event occurred in 8498 B.C., which we refer to for convenience as 10,500 B.P. Because of the asteroid impact, the end of the Ice Age came with unparalleled swiftness. Glacial maximum had been reached at 18,000 B.P. and a slow ending of the Ice Age had begun. After the asteroid impact of 10,500 B.P., the melt rate vastly increased reducing the great glacial sheets, which took 117,000 years to form, to mere remnants by 6500 B.P. Thus they were gone 4,000 years after the asteroid impact. By 6500 B.P., due to glacial melting and other causes, the worldwide sea level had increased an average of 400 feet. Hence it is no surprise that so little in the way of hard archeological material exists as remnants of the First Civilization. The following list is a convenient summary of these destructive forces:

1. North Africa becomes the Sahara desert from 40,000 to 10,500 B.P.

2. An asteroid impact in the North Atlantic at 10,500 B.P.

3. The end of the Ice Age brought about a total change in the world's geography from what it was during the Ice Age to what it is today. This occurred from 10,500 to 6500 B.P.

4. The rising sea level from 10,500 to 6500 B.P.

All of this served to obliterate most of the material evidence of the First Civilization. Probably 90 percent of the civilized Homo sapiens of the world perished because of the asteroid impact. There was a cultural hiatus of about 5,000 years, from 10,500 to 5000 B.P., referred to as the Mesolithic age, followed by a reemergence of retrograde forms of human civilization in the Indus Valley, Tigris-Euphrates, the Nile, and Central America. These prospered for a while and failed. Other civilizations (Arabic, Greek, Roman, and European) continued a hesitant march forward to the present day.

A time period for the First Civilization is needed so as to concentrate thought. The period 40,000 to 10,500 B.P. will be very satisfactory. The ending date is an absolute date as the First Civilization ended when the asteroid struck. The first date is arbitrary but selected for very good reasons. By 40,000 B.P., Homo sapiens was moving around the world. Anthropologists are virtually unanimous that in the Far East, in lands as far away as Australia, Homo sapiens had arrived by 50,000 B.P., traveling overland and by *boat*. Homo sapiens entered the remote lands of Europe from the west by boat between 40,000 and 10,500 B.P. These assumptions are based on evidence from the art caves. These caves have a very precise time frame of 34,000 to 10,500 B.P. The New World was settled by boat (and raft) from North Africa between 20,000 and 10,500 B.P. when all further immigration stopped. This very movement of Homo sapiens around the earth bespeaks civilization as the factor leading to overpopulation. Ships, allied technologies, and adaptability to climate were all involved. Besides Homo sapiens' movement around the world, beginning at 40,000 B.P., a second factor causes us to choose this date as the beginning of the First Civilization; at this time there is a quantum leap in Homo sapiens' art and technology. It is found wherever he traveled. Let us look at a geographical picture of the world from 40,000 B.P. (the first noted traveling by Homo sapiens) to 18,000 B.P. (glacial maximum).

The world was much different than it is now. Large amounts of ice covered North America. The Cordilleran and Laurentide ice sheets were a continuous mass across the continent, the southern boundary being just below the United States-Canadian border with permafrost extending one thousand miles south of that. The continent was inhabited by animals above and below the great ice sheets, but not by man. South America was quite different. What is today the Amazon rain forest was instead a savanna of green country, generally level, with scattered trees and hardy undergrowth. The savanna reached as far as the truly beautiful, rich volcanic ash lands of today's jewel, Ecuador. All of this was reachable by the Amazon River, which was navigable upstream 2,000 miles from its mouth. As in North America, South America was not inhabited by humans, only animals. South America's geography was determined by the weather pattern imposed by the Ice Age. Less precipitation because of ice-age aridity caused the Amazon Basin to become a very desirable savanna instead of the tropical rain forest we know today. And we must at this point disabuse ourselves of a pervasive fallacy; that the equator is too hot a place to live. This is not true. Even today, when it is much warmer along the equator, the equatorial area of the world can be quite a pleasant place to live. The Sun swings to $23^1/2°$ north and south of the equator during the year making the equator only the average of its swing and exceedingly hot only when it is directly overhead. Secondary factors affect the climate either favorably or unfavorably for human occupation: ice-age aridity, present-day tropical rainfall, desertification, elevation above sea level, and proximity to water. At present, we are in an unfavorable time period for the Amazon Basin and the result is an impassable jungle caused by heat and rainfall. Between 40,000 and 10,500 B.P., there was a quite favorable period and the result in South America was a beautiful savanna in the Amazon

Basin, the product of mild aridity.

In Europe, the great ice sheet pressed down covering most of Ireland, England, and continental Europe along a line north of the Pyrenees Mountains and the Alps, turning north in the Balkans, leaving Siberia ice-free but very cold; this was home to millions of animals but no Homo sapiens. The earth also looked vastly different elsewhere. The Atlantic was considerably narrower, as the continental shelves were all exposed and rivers ran to their edges. The average drop from top to bottom of a continental shelf is 12,000 feet. Much of the Mid-Atlantic Ridge was *above* water. It reached its present depth as a result of two events. The most important event was the asteroid impact. The resulting volcanism lowered the seabed along the ridge an average of 10,000 feet. The second determining factor was the general eustatic sea rise by an average of 400 feet, caused by the melting glacial ice.

During the Ice Age the weather on the Atlantic Ocean was more severe than it is now. Drift ice moved farther south, to the mid-United States (latitude 40°). The Canary Current was stronger and swifter as was the Gulf Stream. And the Gulf Stream did not reach Europe. It ended at the Mid-Atlantic Ridge, at the Azores, causing Europe to be cold and glaciated, not warm as it is now due to the warming influence of the Gulf Stream. Ice-age weather in general was more vigorous—again a direct product of the great ice sheets.

Until 40,000 B.P. in North Africa the climate remained beneficial to Homo sapiens. Thereafter increasing aridity changed the landscape from forest to grasslands and the temperature steadily dropped but very little by comparison to other areas of the world. In North Africa, temperature drop from pre-Ice Age (or today's) conditions was only about 4°F. (In England the drop was about 12°, making it as cold as northern Alaska.) North Africa was the perfect place for the development of modern man. The Ice Age caused focus on this area as the most desirable place in the world for man to live. It was an oasis in a world with one-third of its land covered by ice and one-half of its oceans affected by pack ice and floating ice. But man's population soared during this time and large numbers had to leave. There is ample evidence of the exodus to the east, and Homo sapiens' invasion of Europe into Neanderthal Territory (starting around 40,000 B.P.) are both clear manifestations of overpopulation, as is the later migration to the New World (20,000 to 10,500 B.P.).

Above we have outlined the geography of North and South America and North Africa relative to the beginning of the First Civilization at 40,000 B.P. North Africa was at that time highly favorable to man's development. By glacial maximum at 18,000 B.P. things had changed greatly for the worse, and due to aridity, North Africa, the cradle of man's First Civilization had become an impossible place to inhabit—except along its northwest seacoast fringe and the Nile River; man had to leave and live elsewhere. It is a picture of constant emigration out of North Africa from before glacial maximum to an abrupt end at 10,500 B.P.; it seems that at first the direction emphasized was to the east, then north to Europe, then west to the New World. But exactly where could man go? The great ice sheets and permafrost had taken away one-third of the earth's land. Aridity, exacerbated by the Ice Age, had turned one-third of the earth's land into desert, most of which was in the tropics; it included North Africa, man's homeland, which became the Sahara desert. The reality is that man did not have many options. To the east was desert. Good land was far away and unknown, a difficult overland journey. Europe was cold and forbidding, in the grip of the ice. South America was the best choice, but a fearsome boat ride away. It is obvious that man would not leave North Africa unless he had to. Aridity and overpopulation forced him to leave.

Anthropologists and paleohistorians would prize beyond words the briefest glimpse of the beginnings of man's First Civilization. Unfortunately there is none to offer. A great number of disparate facts exist that relate to man's first incipient civilization. With knowledge of these and the addition of more facts, perhaps a clearer picture will emerge. First and foremost is the principle that the Ice Age was responsible for man becoming civilized. Ice Age weather in North Africa was vigorous, hot and cold to very cold, and quite changeable in a rather short time. Man, a tropical animal, had to adapt to the cold. With a generalized body, he needed clothes, a meat diet and artificial shelter. Only by interpersonal contact could this be done. Thus, the cold and a hunter-gatherer lifestyle began to encourage greater social organization, the development of better means to achieve survival, and beyond that, a better life. It takes a long time to develop a civilization, and it takes a large population; such a population requires a large amount of food leading to the development of agriculture and the domestication of animals. Unfortunately, religion helps in advancing developing civilizations; not because it contains any truth, but because it is an excellent organizer of large groups of people, akin to the military. A favorable environment was required to provide the necessities of such an emerging civilization and North Africa had it. As the Ice Age began its progression from the beginning of the first interglacial (130,000 B.P.) to glacial maximum (18,000 B.P.), the time of the greatest cold and most extreme aridity, the North African forests gave way to open woodlands and vast grasslands—a perfect environment for an emerging civilization.

Homo sapiens was more than ready to take advantage of the opportunity. He was fully human at 150,000 B.P. and superior to today's man both mentally and physically. We cannot track his efforts in domesticating the first animal, planting the first crop, building the first building, or launching the first ship. The best we can do is search back in the archaeological record, looking for the earliest domesticated animals, crops, buildings, a ship, but when we find one, ancient man has already been there, for an unknown period of time. Most scholars admit that the origins of domestication of animals and crop planting are unknown, lost in the distant past. About 40,000 B.P., the date we chose as the beginning of an established civilization, the archaeological record comes alive. One anthropologist and paleohistorian, Richard Carrington, in *A Million Years of Man,* calls this the time of "an explosion of the mind." Man begins to travel the world, and he uses boats to do so. The art caves begin at 34,000 B.P. and are a product of Homo sapiens, now invading Neanderthal Territory. The artistic product arrived in full flower, no buildup, evidence of a very mature people who wore cloth clothing not animal skins, and who probably obtained some of the pigments from Africa, where chromium and hematite ores were used to make brilliant colors. In Europe, countless artifacts, tools, and artwork are found contemporaneous with the art caves. Stone teeth for sickles are found after 20,000 B.P. Mid-Stone Age individual and communal dwellings are found in the Balkans. And finally in one stroke we know the North African civilization is complete—man populates the New World. A very recent discovery at Cactus Hill, 45 miles south of Richmond, Virginia has been conclusively dated to 18,000 years old. Monte Verde in southern Chile is dated at 13,000 years ago. Unique soil conditions have left the site remarkably well preserved. The site shows evidence of a very sophisticated people. It includes wooden foundations, the remains of berries and plants that would provide food all year, and tubers that appear to be cultivated. Mastodons and small animals provided meat.

The group cooked communally. The archaeologist in charge, Tom D. Dillehay, suggests strongly that we rethink the date of the arrival of the first immigrants to the New World and suggests 20,000 B.P. as a rough date since the Pikimachay Cave in Peru and Meadowcroft Rock Shelter in Pennsylvania have artifacts dating from 20,000 to 15,000 B.P. The only possible way such early arrivals could have come to the New World was by boat, and that requires a mature civilization to be established on the east side of the Atlantic Ocean.

CHAPTER 12: ACCOMPLISHMENTS OF THE FIRST CIVILIZATION

We now search for hard archaeological evidence of the First Civilization and return later in "Part V: Man Recovers," to an analysis of the reemergent civilizations of the Near East, Egypt, and the Americas. At that time, we will look for cultural and scientific legacies of the First Civilization. The present task is hard because the First Civilization was virtually totally destroyed by the asteroid impact. However, there are certain clues to follow in our search. Man originated in East Africa. Homo sapiens occupied North Africa during his earliest stage of development. If he left this location, it would be to occupy ground that better suited his needs. It has been said that "man lives in the wet spots of the world." We need to know the Ice Age weather pattern, roughly outlined in the previous chapter, so that we may anticipate where to look. At the height of the Ice Age (glacial maximum 18,000 B.P.), the land available as suitable habitat for man is a much smaller area of the earth than at present. The ice and permafrost covered one-third of the landmass of the world and desert was rapidly forming in another one-third as the result of aridity. Given the need to find usable land and obtain desired items, the easiest way to search would have been by boat.

We will find the First Civilization was a very great maritime civilization. As the outstanding anthropologist Thor Heyerdahl observed, the ocean currents have been highways for man, and civilizations inevitably are found at the ends of such currents. There also is the advantage of certain known dates that help us visualize the growth and problems of the First Civilization. These are:

1. Homo sapiens' settlement of Australia and environs beginning at 50,000 B.P.

2. Homo sapiens' immigration into Ice Age Europe from 40,000 to 10,500 B.P.—confronting the prior settlers, the Neanderthals. (The Neanderthals became extinct by 20,000 B.P.)

3. The art caves 34,000 to 10,500 B.P.

4. The New World is settled from 20,000 to 10,500 B.P.

5. The end of the First Civilization: the asteroid strike at 10,500 B.P.

6. The oceans rise from 10,500 to 6,500 B.P.

7. "The Gap" 10,500 to 5,000 B.P. The Mesolithic age, a regressive time in man's culture. In many archaeological finds (for example, the ancient cyclopean stone walls of South America), there is a noticeable difference in age between the first artifacts and subsequent ones (that is later structures built on top of the earlier walls). This 5,000-year gap between the time of construction of the first walls and the later structures is often noticeable and a clear clue to the work product of the First Civilization.

8. Four civilizations reemerge at 5,000 B.P.

Our best shot is to itemize some of the clear accomplishments of the First Civilization. We cannot weave these accomplishments into the chronological pattern so dear to historians, nor can we always produce from the ground a solid artifact so dear to archaeologists. But we will avoid imagination, speculation and hypothesizing as much as possible—and stick to the facts. The question is then: What can we now see as Homo sapiens' physical accomplishments from 40,000 to 10,500 B.P.?

The first and foremost fact we must accept is that the First Civilization was a maritime world imbued with awesome scope and the ability to explore the oceans of the entire world. A touchstone of proof of this vast maritime civilization is the work of professor Charles Hapgood presented in his book *Maps of the Ancient Sea Kings*. This absolutely amazing book presents maps whose provenance predates 10,500 B.P. The beginning of these exciting discoveries occurred in 1929 when an old map was found in the ancient Imperial Palace in Constantinople. It was dated 1513 by the Christian calendar and the author was an admiral of the Turkish Navy named Piri Reis. The map is a rendering of the eastern seacoast of the Americas (from Artic to Antarctic) and of the western seacoast of Europe and Africa from Spain to the equator. Therefore, the whole Atlantic had been mapped, but unfortunately, the Piri Reis map was torn and most of the European-African side was lost. The map is accurate and yet it is a great mystery. Between the time of Columbus' discovery of the Americas in 1492 and 1513 when the map appeared, very little of this coastline had been explored, much less mapped. Piri Reis stated he used ancient maps to create his single map, but these are lost.

The finished map contained many quirky medieval notes and other evidence of added information but the core of the map is astounding: it is based on spherical trigonometry; it has both latitude and longitude; it shows a good part of the continent of Antarctica accurately and as *ice-free*! In 1513 the science of spherical trigonometry was completely unknown to man. In all of history, it had been only hinted at once in Alexandria by the Greek mathematician Ptolemy in the second century A.D. Modern-day man first applied it after the work of Descartes and others (1637). Knowledge of spherical trigonometry was essential to map the earth, as it is a globe. Longitude lines merge at the pole, and a flat map must properly reflect this rounding effect. Longitude is properly shown on the Piri Reis map and the others presented by Professor Hapgood. Longitude is the distance east or west from a prime meridian. A degree of longitude decreases in proportion to the distance between the equator and the pole. To compute longitude a mapmaker on a ship needs to know the size of the earth, the speed of its rotation, what latitude he is on, and the time locally (high noon will do), and local time on the prime meridian. The last requirement was difficult; it required a clock to keep accurate time at sea, something a pendulum clock could not do. In 1714, the English parliament authorized a prize of £20,000 to solve the problem of longitude. John Harrison (1693–1776) won with a clock powered by a spring. So how did the makers of Professor Hapgood's maps measure longitude accurately when the Greeks could not do it, sailors of Columbus' time could not do it, and the Royal Navy could not do it until 1714? We do not know, because without a clock it is almost impossible.

The Piri Reis map and especially the Oronteus Finaeus map (drawn by him in 1531) show Antarctica; the Piri Reis map shows the continent only in part, and the Oronteus Finaeus map shows the entire landmass. Present-day man did not "discover" Antarctica until 1773 when Cook

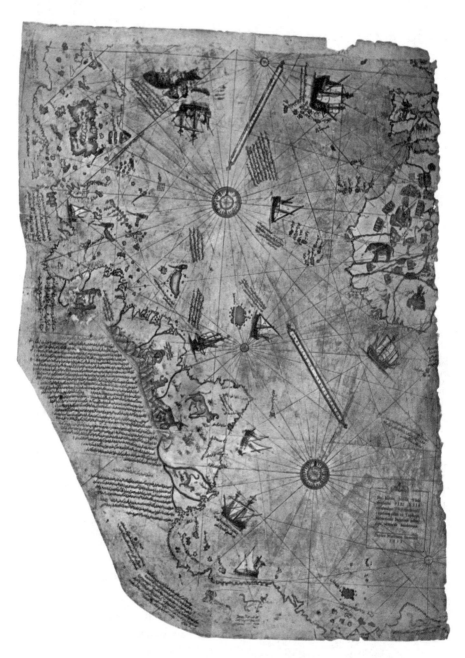

This map was created by Turkish Admiral Piri Reis in A.D. 1513 from older maps (now lost) at his disposal. It accurately shows the then unexplored eastern coast of South America and part of the Antarctic that had not yet been discovered. *Maps of the Ancient Sea Kings,* Charles H. Hapgood

Rediscovered in the United States Library of Congress in 1960 by Professor C. H. Hapgood, the map drawn by Oronteus Finaeus in A.D. 1531 correctly maps Antarctica from now lost sources with accurate longitude and latitude. Correct placement of rivers and mountains (now ice-covered) show that at the time the original map was made, Antarctic was largely ice-free. Europeans rediscovered Antarctica in the early 1800s. *Maps of the Ancient Sea Kings,* Charles H. Hapgood sailed within 75 miles of the continent. Cook did not recognize it as a continent due to the obscuring pack ice; he did not claim the discovery because he did not really prove it was there.[13] The ancient mapmakers knew it was there because they mapped it. And, unbelievably, they mapped it when it was free of ice except for a probable mid-continent ice sheet. All of this coast and inland area is now covered with glacial ice over one mile thick. Snow deposits turn into far more compact ice in about twenty years, and as Antarctica is a desert, on average a foot of snow or less falls from the sky per year. It would take more than 10,000 years to accumulate this mass of ice. Thus, we can gage the ancient age of the map. The same phenomenon is true of Greenland. In 1380, two Venetians, Niccole and Antonio Zeno sailed into the North Atlantic (exactly where they sailed we do not know), but they possessed a map of the North Atlantic showing the coasts of Norway, Sweden, Denmark, Scotland, Iceland, and Greenland. It is accurate in latitude and longitude. It shows Greenland largely covered with ice but with mountains and rivers (the latter especially in appropriate places). Records and archaeological work relating to the early Norse settlement show that the Greenland ice cap is expanding, just as is the Antarctic ice cap. The maps would show Greenland, as it was long before 10,500 B.P.

The maps just discussed were made for a purpose—maritime use. From these maps we may deduce many things. First, there were people with exceptional knowledge of the earth, astronomy, mathematics, who made the maps. It took a long period of time to acquire this education, schools to teach it, and an economic need for the map product. When these maps were made, a highly cultured civilization existed. The next step is to look at the practical application of the maps by studying ships.

One heroic individual stands out as an authority on ancient ships, Thor Heyerdahl. Famous as an adventurer, he is often overlooked as a world-class anthropologist; he has all the credentials, including a Ph.D. and over seventy scientific papers published. Popular books of his adventures on the sea serve the purpose of awakening the layman to thinking about man's past as an exciting endeavor not a dry monologue of dates and places (and the books pay the bills). But many others have also contributed to our knowledge of ancient ships and shipping and to summarize this collective work is a daunting task. Our concern is with ships and seafaring before 10,500 B.P. Professor Hapgood's maps and the known movements of people by sea, prove that there were

John Cogan

ships and worldwide seafaring before this time. However, we lack archaeological evidence of the ships themselves. This is no surprise as ships are perishable structures. But we have one great advantage here—ship design is virtually timeless and a classic design will last for many thousands of years. Thus, we can fairly assume that the first ships known to exist after 10,500 B.P. (that is, 5000 B.P.) bear a great resemblance to those before 10,500 B.P.

Heyerdahl believes that the earliest large ship suitable for ocean-going voyages was a ship made of papyrus reed, which was at that time abundant in North Africa. Such ships are shown by petroglyphs to have been in use from the far Mideast, through the Mediterranean Sea, to Atlantic Morocco. Plenty of reed boats were around in Mesopotamia in 1916. English soldiers observed these vessels during the First World War, although these were a smaller variety for local use. Thus, the reed boat has endured 5,000 years from the present back to the earliest time of the Mesopotamian and Egyptian civilizations. Here we encounter "The Gap" back to 10,500 B.P. (the Mesolithic age). During this time period from 5,000 to 10,500 B.P., we expect to find nothing. But it is a very fair assumption to make that the first boats seen in the reemerging civilizations were the same as those of the First Civilization (40,000 to 10,500 B.P.). We know the boats were oceangoing and quite large because they were used to transport people from North Africa to the New World. They were *big!* Heyerdahl reports on ancient Egyptian and Algerian rock carvings and estimates the date of these particular carvings at 6000 to 5000 B.P.:

> One is struck by the fact that the majority of these sickle-shaped vessels has a numerous crew, sometime fifty men or more. In addition to the double steering oar, some show forty or more rowing oars in the water, while a considerable number have mast and rigging and in many cases a large hoisted sail. The great dimensions of these vessels are indicated not only by the men and oars, but also by the fact that horned cattle and other large animals are dwarfed on their decks. It is not uncommon that one, or even two, cabins are shown on deck, one fore and one aft of the mast.
>
> Thor Heyerdahl, *Early Man and the Ocean*, p 6.

Another authority reports Egyptian ships of 250 feet in length. The Sumerians of Mesopotamia (6000 to 5000 B.P.) are recorded as having vessels of 100-ton displacement. The later (and upriver) Babylonians (4000 to 3000 B.P.) had ships, described in tablets, capable of carrying over 50 tons of cargo. Not only did the ancients have big ships, it would seem they had standard size ships. The Indus civilization, which traded heavily with Sumer had an 800-mile coastal strip with many seaports, including an exceptional one at Lothal which is reasonably well preserved. It dates to 4300 B.P. and consists of an excavated basin with a movable spillway to trap the high water, an artificial dock, and shoreside warehouses. It was designed to take ships of 59 to 65 feet long and 13 to 20 feet in width.

The art of building seagoing reed ships was lost, however. Heyerdahl built three in all to test their characteristics. The first two, used to sail the Canary Current from Africa to South America, were not totally successful. The reeds were cut in December instead of August and became waterlogged. The third ship corrected the errors of the first two and was completely successful. That ship, the *Tigris*, sailed the Arabian Gulf and the Indian Ocean for five months, covered 4,200 miles with a crew of eleven men and ended the voyage in perfect shape. It was 60 feet long and weighed 33 tons and it carried the equivalent of a 40-foot truck trailer full of provisions and equipment. It took six weeks to build *Tigris*. Unfortunately, it was deliberately destroyed at the end of the voyage. It had been estimated that the ship would last for at least several years. The reed boat proved to be a superb vessel. It was easy to build, very safe on the water, comfortable to handle and capable of great carrying capacity. It was an oceangoing ship, just what the First Civilization needed. As the Sahara dried up, man was forced to leave and reed boats could provide the transportation for thousands of people to the New World. The journey was 1,700 miles and thirty days from North Africa to Brazil or the Caribbean Sea. The reed ship was ideal for the voyage as Heyerdahl proved. When the voyage was over, it could be abandoned with the loss of only some work in its building and a minimal amount of materials. *Ra I*, Heyerdahl's first reed boat made for the Atlantic crossing, took three men six weeks to build, weighed 12 tons dry, was 45 feet long and 15 feet wide and could carry 5 tons of cargo. It had a sail 26 feet high, 23 feet wide at the top and 15 feet at the bottom. The only tools required to build the boat itself, as Heyerdahl succinctly put it, were rope and a knife to cut the rope (a stone knife would do). The *Ra I Expedition* took plenty of food in authentic earthen jars (160 of them), all as part of the experiment. However, it was so easy to catch fish at sea that a minimum of supplies was actually needed. They did not repeat the food experiment on later expeditions because they considered it unnecessary. The expedition could live off the sea.[14]

Then came wooden ships patterned after their reed forebears, possessing only one advantage, greater durability. As papyrus disappeared from Africa, wood became the only choice. An incredible find was made in the late 1960s when a ship 4,600 years old, was found near the Great Pyramid hermetically preserved in a stone chamber. It was of reed boat design ("papyriform") with prow and stern arching gracefully upward 143 feet in length. The wood was cedar, from Lebanon, home to wide-ranging Phoenician seafarers. This particular ship had only been used on the Nile but its design was eminently oceangoing, resembling a Viking ship. Then, incredibly, a fleet of twelve wooden boats 5,000 years old was found at Adyclos in 1991 buried near a pharaoh's mortuary temple. They were 50 to 60 feet long, high-prowed, and made for the open sea. In *Fingerprints of the Gods*, Graham Hancock reports the Cairo Museum has a wall painting of exactly similar ships dating back to 6500 B.P. (p. 40) This is before the generally accepted date for the beginning of the Egyptian civilization. Thus, right from the start the Egyptians were equipped with maps of the Atlantic and seagoing ships. Just like the maps, these ships require a long period of time to develop. The Egyptians had them from the start and show no period of development. These ship finds back right up to The Gap or Mesolithic age—man's dead period, therefore, the provenance of the ships goes back to 10,500 B.P. and before, to the First Civilization.

Another ship of ancient lineage that survived into the present time is the dhow, a sailing ship from the Mideast, Red Sea, Arabian Gulf, and Indian Ocean. Its most characteristic feature is a slanted sail (lateen) that serves to give it a considerable advantage over square sails; it can sail within 60° of the wind. From all this we see that there was no "beginning" to the seafaring tradition; it was always there. In fact, when we consider the worldwide maps of Professor Hapgood, we see definite evidence that the First Civilization was far more advanced in ships and seafaring than has ever been guessed, and it possessed ships that were much stronger, bigger, and navigated more difficult waters with greater certainty, than were seen until very recent time.

The magnificent art caves of Spain and France are products of the

First Civilization. There are approximately 200 of these fabulous caves, both north and south of the Pyrenees Mountains, and collectively, they are one of the wonders of the world. They exist only in western Europe.[15] The art cave period in Europe began suddenly about 34,000 B.P. after the arrival of Cro-Magnon man. Europe had been an exclusively Neanderthal redoubt for 150,000 years, and the Neanderthals produced no art. There was no buildup of artistic proficiency. Cro-Magnons brought the art with them in fully mature form, and what a form it is! It is undoubtedly some of the greatest artwork ever produced by man. It rivals the work of the great masters of the Renaissance and could only have been produced by highly intelligent people thoroughly experienced and schooled in art. The paintings, sculptures, and line drawings of all types of animals and an occasional human are magnificent; however, the art is only part of an ancient cave experience, which produced a cumulative effect by combining art, singing, chanting, music, dancing, magical effects, visual effects, and drama.

The newcomers came from the west by boat entering Europe on both sides of the Pyrenees and made their way inland by following rivers. They did not travel through the Pyrenees because of massive ice-age glaciations. The Cro-Magnons overlapped in time with the Neanderthals from 34,000 to 20,000 B.P. when the latter became extinct. The cave art period ended abruptly at 10,500 B.P. The caves are of limestone and were created by water erosion. Often the cave opening is very small and the best art is found only after a long journey in absolute darkness through large, then small and difficult passages. It is not for the faint of heart. The animals painted in the caves (many of which went extinct at 10,500 B.P. along with the cave painters) are shown with consummate accuracy, whereas the few human figures are caricatures. The painting technique is oil painting at its best. The surface was prepared with fat and oil, then powdered colors were brushed or blown onto the background through blow tubes of bone (a great number have been found). Mortars were used to pound the ochre (impure iron ore, earthy and in shades of red and yellow). At the Mas I'Azil and Altamira Caves (and others) ochre crayons have been found neatly lined up with colors ranging from light to dark. Cave art was obviously highly organized, respected, carefully done by craftsmen who had studied art, and it appears some of the pigment used came from Africa. There is evidence of a school at Altamira.

What was the purpose of the caves? They were not lived in. Many show the footprints of children. At Trois-Fre'res there is the famous "sorcerer," a man in animal skins that adds a smell of ice-age religion. But the simplest explanation is probably the best—a place for memory implantation. Nonliterate man had a prodigious capacity for memory. But it is a learned skill, and we contemporary moderns with access to books have lost it. Teachers of the Middle Ages used to take students through the cathedrals, so that the students could associate a place in the cathedral with what they were told. The most important facts were told at the beginning, giving rise to the expression "in the first place." The art caves are perfectly suited for this use that was vital and important to convey knowledge to nonliterate people of high intelligence. We must remind ourselves that these people had IQs higher than our own. There is some pathos in studying the art caves. Overall, they show a people under stress. The Cro-Magnons were immigrants to Europe, and the numbers increased as time passed. Although the cave art started at 34,000 B.P., roughly 80 percent of the art was accomplished between 15,000 and 10,500 B.P. indicating an acceleration of population buildup during this time. There was a large overpopulation in North Africa that fed the migration into Europe. North Africa was drying up and the increased immigration to Europe coincides exactly with the immigration to the New World, as we shall see.

The area north and south of the Pyrenees Mountains that contain the vast majority of the art caves was very much in the grip of the Ice Age from 34,000 to 10,500 B.P. The Pyrenees was heavily glaciated and the great European ice sheet was nearby to the north covering much of Ireland, England, and France then curving toward the northeast. In between the glaciers it was very cold with short summers and long winters. Neanderthal man had lived there for 150,000 years and, being short and sturdy, was physically suited to the climate. Accustomed to a tropical habitat, Cro-Magnon man had to adjust to the harsh living conditions of the sub-Pyrenees country. He did so remarkably well. But we need to ponder the fact that Homo sapiens of the tropics made

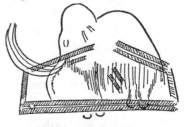

Europe was a frontier for North Africans that were leaving the drying Sahara. The trap demonstrates a high-level of intelligence, social skills, and adaptability to a different environment. Both the cave painters and the mammoth became extinct in 10,500 B.P. *Credit: Reproduction of a cave drawing*

a deliberate choice to live in this harsh country, and moved there in ever-increasing numbers between 40,000 to 10,500 B.P. The struggle for existence was a hard test as hunting and salmon fishing provided the main sustenance, with some gathering of plants, but no agriculture. Fortunately, the area was rich in large game animals and Homo sapiens (Cro-Magnon Man) was an excellent hunter. Cave art depicts the hunting methods used: spears, arrows, "traps, enclosures, palings (fence), lattices, pitfalls, snares . . ." (Herbert Kuhn, *On the Track of Prehistoric Man*, p. 82) One famous painting shows a mammoth in a trap, at Font de Gaume Cave in France. However, this subglacial environment would not be greatly attractive to inhabitants of the tropics. The immigration was a matter of necessity, not free choice. As the Sahara inexorably dried up Homo sapiens had a choice, either the ice-cold frontier (albeit a hunter's paradise) or a voyage across the Atlantic Ocean to a land far away.[16]

The art caves are obviously a frontier of the First Civilization, not representations of its highest achievements. For this we must look elsewhere. Where shall we look for the cities of this civilization, and what do we expect to find? Given Professor Hapgood's maps we know we are dealing with an advanced maritime civilization with North Africa as its focus. We can expect to find evidence of the civilization along the shores of the Indian Ocean, the Mediterranean, and the entire Atlantic Ocean. But the search for hard archaeological finds is almost doomed from the start because of the passage of 10,500 years, the overwhelming catastrophe of the asteroid impact, the desertification of North Africa, man's own destruction of ancient works and written records, and finally, the subsidence of land and rising sea level.

An immediate target is Lixus, Morocco located where the Lucus River enters the Atlantic. This is the start of the Canary Current, which will take a drifting ship to Brazil in thirty days. It is also a perfect port for seafarers venturing from the Mediterranean Sea into the Atlantic. Ancient, gigantic stone ruins still exist. Romans, and long before them the Phoenicians, built structures on the lowest, oldest portions of these ruins. A huge breakwater of tens of thousands of megalithic stone blocks—again age unknown, its creation utterly lost to history—endure to the present, creating an excellent harbor. The city's location is at the eastern edge of ancient caravan trade routes across North Africa. But as Heyerdahl points out in *The Ra Expeditions*, this place of fabulous archaeological potential has so far been almost entirely ignored by archaeologists. Very little work has been done here even though the Romans considered Lixus to be the oldest city in the world and called it the "Eternal City." They believed it to be older than any city inside the Mediterranean Sea. It is this fact that is so astounding about Lixus. It is utterly an Atlantic Ocean seaport (400 miles south of Gibraltar) not at all oriented to the Mediterranean. If it is older than any settlement in the Mediterranean, it must predate 10,500 B.P. and, therefore, is a city of the First Civilization. This defines that civilization's worldwide maritime character and Lixus is clearly the starting point for immigration to the New World. Other cities must be considered as candidates for First Civilization cities, but the case for their antiquity (that is, predating 10,500 B.P.) is not as compelling as Lixus. Tartessos was a city in ancient Spain, a thriving port on the Guadalquivir Estuary at the beginning of the Bronze Age (5000 B.P.) and continued until 2500 B.P. when it was utterly destroyed by the Carthaginians. Its exact location remains unknown, but it had a prior history as well and is very much a candidate for a First Civilization city. On the Atlantic coast, Cadiz, Spain, was founded by Phoenicians from the eastern Mediterranean who needed an Atlantic port. A Bronze Age city, it has an earlier unknown history and is a very likely candidate. The very earliest of man's cities are lost to the Sahara. It is to be hoped that somehow, someway, someday an archaeologist will be lucky and find such an antediluvian pearl. In the meantime, we will concentrate on Lixus.

At Lixus, Heyerdahl was awed at the quality of the most ancient stonework. It was better than any of the later stonework by Phoenicians, Romans, or Arabs and the blocks used were immensely larger and all were cut and polished with joints accurate to a millimeter. Absolutely no known people were capable of such construction, but the pattern is worldwide. Heyerdahl mentions Egypt, Sardinia, Mexico, Peru, and Easter Island as examples. Other authors such as David H. Childress add South America, and he singles out Cuzco, the Inca capital as a showpiece of incredible stone-building technique. At Cuzco, the fortress of Sacsay Luaman is built of gigantic stone blocks, some weighing 200 tons (400,000 pounds); the average stone block in the Great Pyramid is 3 tons. The stones are cut and polished, perfectly fit, with some having thirty angles. The Incas have no idea who built the structure, or how they did so. The Incas built their structures on top of the ancient existing ones, which is the way the Spanish found things, until with their usual lack of respect they demolished what they could to build buildings for themselves. Richard Wingate, an archaeologist, has an important insight. He believes the builders of these cyclopean structures used a cement glue to hold the blocks together. Only the front face of the block is closely fitted. The back of the blocks form a *V*, leaving an opening between them. This is filled with high-alumina cement containing iron oxide as a bonding agent making it fast setting and strong. The bond forms interlocking "hairs" altogether so tenacious that under stress, the cement does not break; the rock itself breaks. This technique applies only to the oldest construction. It must have been used for thousand of years but its origin is clearly in the First Civilization and vastly predates all known history, an utterly lost art. A second Andean city worthy of the most careful study is Tiahuanaco, a gigantic fossil city 13,000 feet high, composed of fantastic cyclopean stone structures. Highly respected archaeologists have estimated its age to be 17,000 years. For the first time, from 1927 to 1930, astronomical alignments were used to gage the age of the monuments. Their orientation established the date of construction. Further, animals that became extinct at 10,500 B.P. are carved on an arch known as the Gateway to the Sun namely the Cuvieronius (an elephant-like animal with trunk and tusks), and the Toxodon (a hippolike animal about 9 feet long and 5 feet high). Certainly, Tiahuanaco is a product of the First Civilization.[17]

Closely allied to cities and cyclopean walls and structures is undersea archaeology, a true storehouse of First Civilization artifacts. When the Ice Age ended with the asteroid impact at 10,500 B.P., the oceans were at their lowest point and were to rise 400 feet over the next 4,000 years as a result of the melting ice. From 40,000 to 10,500 B.P. the First Civilization built many structures on the seacoast, and despite the asteroid disaster some remain although heavily damaged, now covered by seawater. Nevertheless, we can hold a very simple concept: any man-made structure under the ocean will be over 10,500 years old. Science has continually improved equipment for undersea exploration and certainly there are many new finds to be made. Here are some that have already been made. Off Bimini, giant blocks of granite were found on Moselle Shoal and hauled by a salvor named Captain Webster to Miami in the 1930s where they became part of the Jupiter Inlet Jetty (really jetties as there are two parallel jetties over one mile long), and are still there to be seen. The hundreds of stones are of various geometric shapes, all trimmed and dressed with many having patterns of drill holes (for some unknown purpose). Wingate believes the blocks came from a building constructed on the shoal at a time when it was above water. The ancient ferrous oxide cement still present on the blocks (it still holds some of them together) attests to the fact that they were once part of a monumental structure. Bimini holds many mysteries. From an airplane, observers have seen straight lines suggesting roads or aqueducts, as well as the outlines of structural foundations, all underwater. Other underwater explorers like Dr. David Zink, J. M. Valentine, and Charles Berlitz have reported almost countless seabed patterns that bespeak human endeavor, but a caveat is in order: the shifting sands can cover up a find in a matter of minutes. To find something and report it is one thing; finding it again and confirming it is another, as water visibility constantly changes. Underwater archaeology is tough stuff. Despite these obstacles, underwater archaeology has an excellent record of finding submerged man-made structures that had been above the sea before 10,500 B.P.[18]

The First Civilization was clearly preoccupied with maritime matters, but inland it had another vital interest, irrigation. As aridity continued to increase in the Ice Age, irrigation became an imperative. In 1933, French archaeologist Pierre Bellair discovered nearly 1,000 miles of underground tunnels used for irrigation in southern Algeria north of the Hoggar Mountains. The tunnels are 10 feet high and 12 feet wide and run in straight lines from the base of cliffs for up to 3 miles in the limestone rock. When were these constructed? It is unknown, but incredibly ancient. Water source? Also unknown, but obviously in the Hoggar Mountains. At present this is about the worst place in the Sahara desert and the climate had to have been much wetter when the structures were built. Such a monumental task requires an organized society, a large population, agriculture, and a religion. The climate of the Sahara from 10,500 B.P. to the present has been total desert. The few intervals of wetter times would hardly justify such an effort. The conclusion becomes inescapable: the tunnels were built by the First Civilization when the Sahara was a good place for humans to live. The period of increasing ice-age aridity from 40,000 to 10,500 B.P. required total attention to the water supply and irrigation projects are to be expected. One can also imagine how dealing with the problem of transporting water advanced Homo sapiens' power of cognitive thinking. The irrigation project was an immense effort. When finished, it supported a great number of people.

The same tunnel construction was found in Armenia and Iran by Sargon II King of Assyria (714 B.C.). Thor Heyerdahl found the same thing in Oman (1979). There the falaj (irrigation tunnels) were dug for untold miles across the desert often incredibly deep, and with a precision of grade so that the water flowed perfectly regardless of surface elevation fluctuations. The origin of the whole engineering project and its construction is utterly lost in time. Again, the project would make no sense if done after 10,500 B.P. By that time, the water source had dried up and the servient land had become utter desert. Irrigation tunnels as described above are a first-class work, the work of a successful and optimistic people who were capable of the enterprise in both engineering and construction, and now gone. Undoubtedly, similar works await archaeological discovery. All over the world there are remnants of other, more recent irrigation systems all of aqueduct and open-ditch design which is inferior to tunnel construction as it is far less permanent and can lose up to 90 percent of the original water through evaporation. Five thousand years ago, irrigation canals covered much of Iraq; the system lasted until the Mongol invasion of 1258 (that is, four thousand years duration). Remnants of this system still exist in the residual canal embankments that cross the country in parallel lines. Such canals require constant maintenance and eventually (perhaps one thousand years) replacement. Open irrigation systems of recent antiquity exist all over the world. Surprisingly, there are more than was ever before believed. Modern radar scanning has provided photographs of utterly unknown systems. A radar image of the Guatemalan jungle taken in 1977 revealed a maze of irrigation canals now completely overgrown by the jungle. The study of ancient irrigation is vitally important, as it is a direct clue to population density. Agriculture plus irrigation can support from 20 to 200 times the number of people that could otherwise inhabit a given area and from this advantage springs civilization itself. Judging from the scope of North African irrigation projects that predate 10,500 B.P., we can safely conclude the First Civilization counted in the millions of people. These irrigation projects, together with cyclopean stoneworks, give us another insight into the First Civilization—its works are superior in quality to the work of the reemerging civilizations that developed after 5000 B.P.

Since we identify irrigation as well accomplished by 10,500 B.P., then we know that agriculture and its concomitant, the domestication of animals, had greatly preceded this time, as both were initially practiced without irrigation. Unfortunately, the beginnings of agriculture, the domestication of animals and irrigation are completely unknown. Our best approach is to cling to the obvious; if we can find and date works by man we know that the subject society is underpinned by agriculture and domestication of animals which long preceded the building of structures. Thus, a few glimpses of archaeological finds are in order and we infer that agriculture, domestication of animals, and irrigation precede the find date. Cave art of both paintings, and carvings has depicted animals with halters and these date to between 30,000 and 20,000 B.P. In the 1890s, Edouard Piette discovered a reindeer bull at Langerie-Bass and a horse with halters at La Pasiega. A carved horse's head with a halter of twisted rope was found at St. Michel d'Arudy in 1893. Archaeologists have found stone sickles and massive grinding stones for grain dated to 19,000 B.P. on the Kom Ombo Plain (twenty miles south of the Aswan Dam in Egypt) and in the southern Sahara. In the New World, the oldest settlement found so far is Monte Verde in southern Chile, carbon-dated at 13,000 B.P. It is an agricultural economy, with a high-cultural level, using cut planks in building construction, cloth for clothing, and in general, a wealth of artifacts showing great sophistication; undoubtedly, these people were pioneers facing a wilderness environment. Consequently, they were far removed from older, higher levels of civilization. New World settlement dates are expected to be verified to 20,000 B.P. Such dates are extremely significant because New World settlement means boats; boats mean a civilization and a civilization means a long prehistory of agriculture, domestication of animals, and irrigation.

After 7000 B.P., countless archaeological finds relative to agriculture appear as man resettles parts of North Africa and Eurasia. This has caused researchers to falsely assume they are observing the origination of agriculture, domestication of animals, and irrigation when, in fact, they are only observing its reemergence caused by people moving back into areas such as the Nile and Tigris-Euphrates basin, which were devastated by the asteroid strike at 10,500 B.P. ·

CHAPTER 13: THE SAHARA DRIES UP

North Africa would appear to be safe from the advancing European ice sheet as it is far away and no direct connection is readily seen. But there is a strong connection very real and very dangerous, the climate. Ice-age weather was unlike our own. It was unstable, changing, often violent, always colder and dryer. This weather pattern itself is a hallmark of the Ice Age just like the enormous glacial ice fields themselves. Early in the Ice Age, the Sahara was a magnificent grassy hunting ground, the home of emerging modern man and his works; however, between 40,000 and 10,500 B.P. it became a desert and resulted in the displacement of great numbers of people who dispersed all over the world.[19]

As we have seen, in the Pleistocene period of 2.4 million years there were four major pulses of glaciations. We are concerned with the last. The third great glacial period ended about 130,000 years ago followed by a warm interglacial. The fourth pulse began about 120,000 years ago. By 70,000 years ago, the great ice sheets were in place but still expanding until glacial maximum at 18,000 B.P. At this time, a slow contraction began and continued intermittently until 10,500 B.P. when a precipitous melt began. The present location of glacial ice was reached at 6500 B.P. Homo sapiens fits rather neatly into this chronology. He appears distinct from his Homo erectus ancestors about 150,000 years ago at the beginning of the last interglacial period. We say without reservation, that from that time to the present, he is in all ways as mentally and physically competent as contemporary man. And well it was that Homo sapiens had such physical and mental capacity, as he would contend with the full measure of the Ice Age. Fortunately, he starts with an interglacial (130,000 to 120,000 B.P.), then comes advancing cold and increasing aridity to the time of glacial maximum (18,000 B.P.), which continues to the abrupt end of the Ice Age at 10,500 B.P. Since Homo sapiens' homeland was East Africa and the Sahara, knowledge of this paleoclimate is necessary to interpret the archaeological record as we track Homo sapiens' cultural development and his travels around the world.

When the third Ice Age ended, an interglacial (Eemain Interglacial 130,000 to 120,000 B.P.) produced a climate in the Sahara extremely suitable to human occupation with ample rainfall, creeks, rivers, trees, grass, and abundant game. After the beginning of the fourth ice pulse (the last occurring Ice Age), the weather was not stable. The warm climate slowly changed to cold as the ice cover and permafrost pushed relentlessly south in Eurasia. Between 40,000 and 10,500 B.P., the human favorable habitat gave way to utterly uninhabitable arid desert. Glacial maximum (18,000 B.P.) came and North Africa suffered the period of maximum cold and maximum aridity, which continued until the Ice Age ended at 10,500 B.P. suddenly and catastrophically with the asteroid impact. The consequences of the impact greatly disrupted the earth's weather. Massive amounts of carbon dioxide were released from the Atlantic Ocean, causing global warming. This led to the precipitous melt of the great ice sheets (10,500 to 6500 B.P.) and at the same time changed the weather pattern over the Sahara. Thus, from 9000 to 6000 B.P., the climate changed to a wetter phase and the environment again became pleasant and habitable, with streams and rivers, trees, grass, forest, and game. Homo Sapiens returned, as is shown by the rock art of the latter part of this period. This art is extensive, covering most of the Sahara. It depicts Black people who are tall, athletic, well-dressed, herding cattle, hunting with bow and arrow, dancing, and in general, exuberantly enjoying life. Unfortunately, this period ended as desiccation returned and the Sahara again became an arid wasteland, as it has remained until today.

The transition from a good human environment to desert was gradual, but the inhospitable future was clearly obvious to the human inhabitants of the Sahara from 40,000 B.P. on. Their lives would be limited. They could only fall back to whatever habitable land remained and that would be around water. Obviously the seacoast on the northwest of Africa and the Nile would be top targets. But the habitable area kept shrinking, almost to nothing. We can only say for sure that there were two places at glacial maximum and thereafter that were well fit for human habitation: the extreme northwest corner of Africa seaward of the Atlas Mountains, and the Nile Valley. However, conditions there were much worse from 18,000 to 10,500 B.P. than they are today. Drill cores from the Nile delta show that during this period the water flow of the Nile was only 10 to 20 percent as large as it is today, a result of lack of rainfall in the catchment area. On the Atlantic side of North Africa the aridity of coastal deserts was exacerbated by the increased upwelling of cold water close to shore caused by the increased atmosphere temperature gradient between the pole and equator, and also by the lower level of the Ice Age oceans. By 10,500 B.P., North Africa was gone to humans. But just how much of the remainder of the earth was available to human habitation? An interesting question with a surprising, yet obvious, answer: not much.

Between 40,000 and 10,500 B.P., when Homo sapiens emigrated from North Africa there were few places to go. Ice and permafrost covered roughly one-third of the earth's land. Deserts occupied another third, mostly in the tropics, and circled the world. Of the remaining one-third much is mountainous, jungle, swamp, isolated, disease-prone, undesirable for other reasons, or already occupied by primitive people. North African man had good reason to go down to the sea in ships and explore the world looking for a place to live. He had to find a new home.

CHAPTER 14: THE NEW WORLD IS SETTLED

The exodus from North Africa was fueled not only by aridity, but also by another factor equally significant, overpopulation. Early man lived in large numbers in Africa.

> The huge quantities of implements at the African sites are an indication of how much at home man must have felt in this tropical paradise and how great his numbers must have been. We went out one Sunday to Olorgosailie, where we spent the whole day. The site lies right down in the Rift Valley depression, nearly 40 miles from Nairobi. Fairly recent movements of the earth's crust have drained an old lake basin at this point; the strata lie at an angle and the surface has been eroded by weathering. Here Leakey found an area about 50 Yards Square on which more than 2,400 Late Acheulian-type hand axes lay about on the ground. He found this accumulation of implements so remarkable that he left them as they were and built over them a raised platform from which the terrain can be surveyed; every stone one sees is a hand ax.
> (G. H. R. von Koenigswald, *Meeting Prehistoric Man*, p. 174).

Hand axes were the tools of primitive man as the Acheulian period ends at the end of the third glacial period. The Acheulian period dates from approximately 1.5 million to 130,000 B.P. Primitive man existed in large numbers even then. As man progressed, his numbers increased even more. The presence of high states of culture with monumental structures indicates the existence of large populations. Since agriculture and domestication of animals can sustain a population of 20 to 200 times larger than without it, there is a symbiotic relationship between man's culture and agriculture and domestication. Each one pushes the other forward. But overpopulation has a dark side. Without question, it leads to war, which gives further social complexity and organization; and, it also leads to religion, which has a similar aspect to war—it is a great organizer. "Religious traditions offer a superbly effective way to get people to act in coordinated ways, because the expenses of large buildings and the 'furs and feathers' of office are cheap, compared to their power in directing the population toward specific economic and political goals." (Robert Wenke, *Patterns in Prehistory*, p. 642) In fact, Professor Wenke sees monumental structures as having the special purpose of dealing with overpopulation: "... we have noted, the primary function of monumental architecture may have been to control populations and organize disparate peoples for collective economic and military action." (p. 576) Increased cultural complexity correlates with population growth. Because the First Civilization had grown and prospered between 40,000 and 10,500 B.P., we know that it was heavily populated. When we see a worldwide emigration pattern as a result of the desertification of North Africa, we know that the environment and population density have collided, and man must seek living space elsewhere. The whole period from 40,000 to 10,500 B.P. is a time of emigration from North Africa. Using the four cardinal points as a guide, a résumé of man's movements follows.

TO THE NORTH In a prior chapter, the art caves were used to define the time of Homo sapiens' movement into Europe. The route was from the west by boat then following rivers inland. The art caves date from 34,000 to 10,500 B.P., with 80 percent of the artwork done between 15,000 and 10,500 B.P.[20] Everything stopped in more than two hundred art caves at precisely 10,500 B.P. Thereafter, there is no art and no immigration. Several thousand years after 10,500 B.P., man reentered Northern Europe but the art caves were forgotten and not rediscovered until 1879. The art caves thus give us an excellent timetable for the emigration from North Africa. But life in the cold below the great European ice sheet was hard. We must appreciate that this is a deliberate choice made by tropically attuned man to live in the cold and survive by strictly hunter gathering. Few people reached thirty years of age because of life's rigors, and there is evidence of conflict over territory. Even in remote Europe, there is again an inference of overpopulation.[21]

TO THE SOUTH There is no discernible immigration into this area. A pullback to habitable country would be expected, but Africa south of the Sahara was occupied. And was it desirable? The western jungle-rain forest would not be and the southwestern part contained more deserts. Only to the far southeast was there desirable land—a long way from the Sahara.

TO THE EAST Homo sapiens had long ventured in this direction (which had been pioneered by Homo erectus before him); Homo sapiens remains have been found in the Levant (lands near the eastern Mediterranean) that date to 100,000 B.P. Similar fossil remains in China date to 70,000 B.P. and man used boats during 50,000 to 40,000 B.P. to populate Indonesia, Australia, and environs. Beginning with 40,000 B.P. and accelerating all the way to 10,500 B.P., there is a new and forceful push toward the east. Between 35,000 to 20,000 B.P. a few hunters enter Siberia for the first time—the frontier of Eurasia and wonderfully filled with game. There is a lot of land to the east of Africa but much of it is desert or mountains, has poor soil or is very cold. Therefore, the population density builds up in the more favored areas as the Nile, Tigris, Euphrates, and Indus and the higher culture remains close to Africa.

TO THE WEST Between 40,000 and 10,500 B.P., North African man's seafaring skills increased to the point that it was possible for thousands of people to cross the Atlantic Ocean on the Canary Current from North Africa to South America and Central America. Nor was it hard to return. The Gulf Stream went north along North America's Atlantic coast but it veered east to Europe on a level with Spain rather than farther north (that is, toward Ireland, England, southern Norway) as it does now. The reason for this is twofold: First, as an effect of the great ice sheets and floating ice that deflected it to the south; second, parts of the Mid-Atlantic Ridge were above water at this time and deflected the Gulf Stream to the south. Hence, a great circular route to the Americas existed.[22] Ocean current would provide the propulsion for any immigrant ship taking it, and maneuvering by sail or oar would be minimized. Navigation required would be basic rather than expert. Certainly the voyage was one way for most immigrants, but obviously some seafarers returned to North Africa thus encouraging others to proceed. And the vessels were there. Rafts of logs or reeds would work well and carry huge cargoes. Reed ships floated like corks and were very safe, probably the choice of those of higher status. Wooden boats were used, fashioned after the reed boats (that is, papyriform), and introduced more frequently toward the end as the reeds became unavailable because of desertification. They would also last much longer and would be more maneuverable in any waters where they encountered drift ice on the return trip.

The drift from North Africa (Lixus was undoubtedly a major starting point) to the Americas is relatively easy. Anthropology is totally in the debt of Thor Heyerdahl for duplicating the crossing. Heyerdahl first became famous for his pioneering balsa raft (Kon-Tiki) crossing of the South Pacific from Ecuador to Tahiti's Raroia reef. The voyage was 4,300 miles long averaging 42 miles per day and took 97 days. The crew of six had all the fish they could eat and had no problems with provisions. The raft had a pointed bow (45 feet from bow to stern) and was composed of nine large balsa logs. It had a reed cabin, sail, steering oars, and five centerboards (keels, movable up and down through the logs). Learning the lost art of using the centerboards was key to handling the raft with ease. The raft was built according to the records of the first Europeans who saw many such crafted rafts off the South American coast. And of course, all academia said no such raft could survive an ocean journey. It did so handsomely, and this led to the ostracism of Heyerdahl by the academic community, which continues to this day. Heyerdahl followed up Kon-Tiki's success with two voyages across the Atlantic in reed boats as detailed in his book, *The Ra Expeditions*. On a third voyage, he sailed the Indian Ocean; this journey is described in *The Tigris Expedition*. Construction plans for the reed boats came from Egyptian wall paintings but the first two reed ships were not really successful—because Heyerdahl had not exactly followed the "engineering" of the ship (rope attachments), and he unknowingly cut the reeds in December instead of August causing them to become waterlogged. He corrected these deficiencies on his third reed ship, the *Tigris*, which was completely successful.

This little summary of Heyerdahl's efforts is given to point out that Heyerdahl has conclusively proven that absolutely nothing stopped ancient man from crossing the Atlantic on the Canary Current, and he reenacted the feat before our very eyes. Professor Hapgood's maps show us that ancient man was far more capable at seafaring than a mere drift voyage on the Canary Current. He accurately mapped the entire Atlantic Ocean using proper latitude and longitude. Heyerdahl's contribution is outstanding because it shows that common items, rafts and reed boats, could take thousands of people across the Atlantic Ocean and populate the New World.[23]

The goal of the North African emigrants was the Amazon Basin, drained by the Amazon River, the mightiest river in the world. It flows almost 4,000 miles from the Andes Mountains on the Pacific Coast across Brazil to the Atlantic Ocean. It is the largest river in the world in terms of volume (it carries 20 percent of all the river water of the world and discharges 170 billion gallons of water per hour into the Atlantic or ten times that of the Mississippi). Its drainage basin area (also called "catchment area"), is 2,722,000 square miles, or as big as the lower forty-eight states of the United States. Over 1,000 tributaries flow into it from the Guiana Highlands to the north and the Brazilian Highlands to the south. Its mouth is 150 miles wide, and the largest modern oceangoing vessels can go 1,000 miles up the river; smaller craft drawing 18 to 20 feet can go 2,300 miles to the present city of Iquitos any time of year. The gradient of the Amazon River is amazingly low; at present, the low water level at Iquitos is only 985 feet above the Atlantic. Suffice to say there is plenty of room here for immigration and settlement and the easiest form of transport, boats, can be used as opposed to a land journey which is always much harder and more dangerous.

During the period 40,000 to 10,500 B.P., the climate of the Amazon Basin was vastly different than today's. The world's temperature and precipitation were at the lowest levels and ice-age aridity that was destroying North Africa as human habitat was also drying the Amazon Basin to a semiarid environment. This resulted in open savanna woodlands and grasslands. Forest cover was greatly restricted, and there was little or no tropical rain forest. The tropical rain forest developed upon the earth's return to higher temperatures and increased precipitation (10,500 B.P. to present). This, in turn, would serve to spread man throughout all of South America, as tropical rain forest is not desirable human habitat. The savanna environment found by the North Africa immigrants was wonderfully suited for game, fishing, plant gathering, and agriculture. It singularly compares with the Sahara as it was early on in the Ice Age as a favorable place for humans to live.[24]

As the Canary Current reaches South America, it splits. The main part washes Brazil then turns north. Its northern edge, however, flows unobstructed into the Caribbean. It took a minor number of voyagers there —most on purpose, some accidentally—and it set the settlement pattern in the New World. It is estimated that there were 42,000,000 Native Americans in the Americas in A.D. 1492. Thirty million lived in South America; 10,000,000 in Central America; and 2,000,000 in North America.

The oldest archaeological sites are in South America, next Central America, and last North America—which was the last land area of the Americas to be settled. Thus, it is fair to say that the demographics of 1492 give us an indication of the original settlement of the New World, and it fully follows the pattern expected of voyages across the Atlantic following the Canary Current. When did the migration occur? We know when it ended. It ended with the asteroid strike of 10,500 B.P., and except for occasional contacts from east and west was not renewed until 1492. Its beginning is hard to measure with exactness. Proof depends upon archaeological data and although an immense amount is available for study, the timing of the settlement of the New World is still a confused matter. In Chile, a site called Monte Verde was reported by archaeologist Tom D. Dillehay in the October 1984 issue of *Scientific American* magazine in an article titled, "A Late Ice Age Settlement in Southern Chile." The site has been carbon dated to 13,000 B.P. The site was located on a creek in a forest near the ocean. Twelve wooden habitable structures were excavated at the time of the article (since then more have been found). The economy of the settlement depended upon big game hunting (mastodons, paleocamedit—an ancestor of the llama, alpaca, vicuña, and others), plant gathering, and agriculture strongly suggested by remains of tubers especially the wild potato. Searchers found bola stones, many grinding stones, mortars, and hundreds of wooden artifacts. Given its location Monte Verde is clearly a frontier outpost of a South American settlement. Yet it shows a high degree of social organization and perfect adaptation to a hunter-gathering, proto-agriculture environment and serves as positive proof of the successful settlement of man throughout South America. In North America, two dates are firmly established as archaeological milestones: Clovis 12,000 B.P. and Folsom 11,000 B.P. These names and dates refer to the discovery of beautifully wrought stone spear points and arrowheads in New Mexico. These were used to hunt the mammoth and the giant bison, now extinct. The Clovis points are regarded as the earliest *certain* date for man in North America and are found all over the non-glaciated land of North and South America. After the Monte Verde date of 13,000 B.P. and the Clovis date of 12,000 B.P., archaeological dates of human activity proliferate, but what about before these dates? There is substantial proof that man was in the Americas long before that (as the ruins of Cuzco and Tiahuanaco attest), but in small numbers. There must have been a great influx of settlers from about 15,000 to 10,500 B.P.[25] This timing would accord well with the known increasing desertification of the Sahara and the immigration of man from the west into Europe as shown by the art caves. The art caves began as early as 34,000 B.P., but 80 percent of the work in the caves was done between 15,000 and 10,500 B.P. This would indicate increasing population density during this period until 10,500 B.P. when immigration to both Europe and the Americas ended. Europe and the Americas thus have a parallel pattern of immigration starting at about the same time and both ending at exactly the same time. We must also note that the archaeological record shows that all the New World was settled by 10,500 B.P.

CHAPTER 15: BERINGIA DID NOT HAPPEN

At this point we must make a digression. It is necessary to dispose of a pernicious theory that has infected anthropology for fifty years, sometimes called the Beringia theory, which holds that Asians crossed a land bridge (which is now the Bering Sea) and populated the Americas during the Ice Age. No such migration ever occurred, and the idea is supported only by speculation, not evidence. The available real evidence conclusively refutes this theory, and this chapter will provide an outline of facts that prove Native Americans are not the result of a migration of Asians during the Ice Age.

I. DEFINITIVE FACTS
Each of the following three facts independently refutes the Asian immigration theory.

A. Blood Type
All Native Americans have blood type O. Asians have either blood type A or B. There is no blood type O in Asia.

B. Demographics
In 1492, Columbus discovered two continents inhabited by 42 million Native Americans. 30 million inhabited South America; 10 million lived in Central America and the Caribbean Islands; only 2 million lived in North America.[26] Spanish destruction and slaughter with continued persecution and disease, makes accurate demographics impossible but the demographic outline is clear. The demographics prove that the point of origin of the expanding Native American population in the Americas was upper South America and Central America, because these are the locations of the highest cultural achievements. By 1492 the

South American native population was widely spread out. Obviously, the point of origin of Native Americans is South America and not the southern terminus of the theoretical ice chute (Ice-Free Corridor) leading from Alaska to Wyoming, as there never was any population density there at all.

C. **No Asian Immigration Artifacts Have Been Found**

For over fifty years archaeologists, aided by thousands of people, have looked for immigration artifacts in the Ice-Free Corridor and found *none. None!!* Not even *one!!* All of this massive effort then disproves the Asian immigration theory. If enough people had journeyed down the hypothetic corridor (its geographical location is quite specific) to produce a population of 42 million in 1492 they would have left a great deal of evidence of this passage, but absolutely none has been found. All corridor artifact finds are Holocene (10,500 B.P. to present), and are of indigenous Native Americans, and the oldest finds are either above or below the great ice sheets.[27]

II. SECONDARY FACTS

The following facts separately and collectively add weight to the demise of the Beringia theory.

A. **Secondary Physical Characteristics**

Asians have oriental eyes, Native Americans have occidental eyes; Asians have yellow skin, Native Americans have copper-colored skin; many Native Americans are rangy, tall, and athletic. This physical type is not commonly found in Asia.

B. **Oral Tradition**

All Native American traditions say their forebears came from the east never the north.

C. **No Asian Ancestors or Present-Day Relations**

No anthropologist has ever identified the location in Asia of the ancestors of Native Americans. (No individuals with type O blood, copper-colored skin, occidental eyes, tall, and athletic have ever been found in Asia.) Neither do any people live in Asia today that would be said to be the modern descendants of such ancestors.

D. Language

In 1492, there were over 400 separate languages (mutually unintelligible) extant in North and South America. None relates to any Asian language.

E. Culture

The Mayan culture relates to no Asian culture, neither does the Inca or Mexican cultures, nor does any American culture (such as, Great Plains etc.) relate to any Asian culture.

F. Dogs

The only domestic animal common to Asia and the Americas in 1492 is the dog. No American dog relates to any Asian dog.[28]

III. ANALYSIS OF THE MIGRATION JOURNEY ITSELF

A. Settlement of North America

North America was settled by Native Americans who moved south to north. A great agricultural civilization, an extension of Middle American influence went from south to north on the east side of the Mississippi River. Other Indians had traveled farther and followed the receding ice. As stated above the North American population was only 5 percent of the inhabitants of the Americas in 1492, about two million people, and they came from the south not the north; no one appeared out of the ice.

B. Settlement of Siberia

Using a very rough measurement, Siberia was settled about the same time as North America (very *sparsely* settled). There was no overpopulation or other motive to cause the people to move south through 3,000 miles of ice into the unknown. (Game was plentiful in the Siberian North during the Ice Age).[29]

C. The Migration Must Have Occurred before 12,000 B.P.; before Clovis

The Clovis (12,000 B.P.) and Folsom (11,000 B.P.) points are found throughout North America south of the ice and South

America, so the New World was completely settled at this time. All subsequently dated artifacts are of resident indigenous Native Americans—no migration trail. So the migration had to have occurred before 12,000 B.P. if it did occur at all; but there is absolutely no evidence of it. If it had to occur before 12,000 B.P., there was a 3,000-mile wall of ice south of Alaska blocking entry into the Americas. The ice did not melt until 10,500 to 6500 B.P.

D. The Ice Free Corridor

It is extremely doubtful it ever existed. It supposes a 3,000-mile north-south separation of the Cordilleran and Laurentide ice sheets running from Alaska to Wyoming through Alberta, Canada. Any closing of the ice would block travel. It was closed until the great sheets began to recede at (10,500 B.P.), too late for the theoretical migration, which had to occur before 12,000 B.P. Even if such a corridor existed it would not sustain life. There were no flora or fauna and constant katabatic winds (descending cold air from the 10,000-feet-high ice sheets, often 100 miles per hour and sometimes 200 miles per hour). Bare rock and water everywhere. No shelter. No food. No fire. No artifacts because: No Life.[30]

E. Travel Kit

No anthropologist has suggested the makeup of the migrants' travel kit. Lacking ability to describe how a human family lives in such conditions, and artfully evading this question is the status of anthropology today. Specifics, not generalities are required. What game was hunted, what plants eaten, what fuel burned, what shelter used, what shoes worn, what weapons used?[31] If people preferred to live in the corridor and merely bred themselves out the south end of it then where is the archeological evidence of such living? There is none.

F. Navigation and "Relation Back"

Hunter-gathers must intimately know their territory in order to survive. They carefully pass on this knowledge to the next generation; and they will fiercely defend their hunting-gathering ground. A journey is an enormous threat. Yet this proposed journey was supposedly undertaken by primitive people without benefit of knowing where they were going other than down an ice chute with no guide and no word from those who had gone before them. Were they dead or alive? A unique migration! At this point the Asian migration theory verges on the absurd.

G. Panama and South America

The Asian migrants left no artifacts at the entry to, within, or at the exit of the hypothetical Ice-Free Corridor. Since 75 percent of them continued on to South America, they passed through Panama; therefore, this would be a logical spot to again look for artifacts of the immigration trail. There are none. Again, there are only indigenous Native American artifacts. In South America we find the oldest archeological sites and by far the largest number of Native Americans. In Central America we find an incredibly advanced culture which does not relate at all to any culture found in Asia. Neither is there any relation to Asia in the choice of 95 percent of the cold-weather attuned Asian immigrants to abandon temperate North America and continue into the tropics with a great number settling in the Yucatán jungle; the worst possible choice they could make. In fact, it makes no sense at all, and to suggest it is to depart from speculation into imagination.

H. The End of the Migration

With the melting of the great ice sheets (10,500 to 6500 B.P.) the route from Alaska to temperate North America and all of Central and South America was now open, supplied with all the requirements of life, but no Asian migrants appear. (About 5000 B.P., Eskimos appear from Asia, encounter Indians and do not proceed south). Water in the Bering Sea is immaterial as it is only 60 miles wide and is frozen six months of the year; it can be crossed. But the big point is the 3,000 miles of ice is gone, and a fertile world awaits, but no Asian immigrants appear. Because there never were any Asian immigrants.

CONCLUSION The artifact record tracts from 12,000 B.P. to the present and proves that there has been no Asian migration to the Americas during this time. The archeological record before this time, although incomplete, is also bare of any evidence of an Asian migration. The inescapable conclusion is that the great ice sheets blocked any migration from north to south. The Ice-Free Corridor hypothesis is false and the basis for suggesting it is only speculation. There is no evidence that it existed, or if it did, that Asian migrants ever used it.[32]

Historical migrations have been observed and there is always a large population base, a motive for the migration and plenty of cultural and physical evidence of its occurrence. Migrants don't go unless they know (roughly) the required navigation, how to travel the journey, and where it will end. Take for example, the European migration to the United States. The large population on the East Coast clearly defines the point of entry; the rest followed. None of this would apply to the proposed Asian migration to the Americas thus making it all the more suspect. Advocates of the theory are reduced to asserting that the migration occurred because of the casual wandering of a few hunting bands (which is a wholly inadequate basis to accomplish the facts of 42 million Native Americans, some enjoying the highest culture in the world, with a decidedly South American demographic emphasis).

Based on speculation and imagination only the Beringia theory has no facts to support it. This is the absolute bottom of scientific inquiry and is not worthy of being called "scientific." The theory is obviously wrong and must be discarded. Its continuance is a disaster for anthropology, creates tunnel vision and precludes an open-minded examination of the history of the populating of the Americas. In a later section of this book, "Part V: Man Recovers," the Beringia theory will be further disproved. It will be shown that the cultural commonalities (and there are hundreds) of the high civilizations of the New World relate clearly and directly to the high civilizations of the Nile and Tigris-Euphrates basins but not to Asia.

Part IV: The Asteroid

CHAPTER 16: SPACE

Space is a dirty and busy place. Our universe is the product of an explosion, the "big bang" that occurred 15 billion years ago. Our solar system is much younger, 5 billion years old and is the product of a supernova, a star that exploded into an immense gas cloud that, in turn, coalesced into our Sun and nine planets. The consequences of the supernova explosion are still with us. And it would be quite an error to believe that our solar system has settled down to the point of becoming static, although all observations indicate that the solar system is well along toward stability after its chaotic beginning. The solar system itself was formed by collisions; collisions of matter formed from the nebula dust, creating ever bigger objects and sweeping areas of space around the Sun clean which would become the locations of planets in orbit. Nine planets eventually formed around the Sun, and there is a certain orderliness throughout the solar system, all due to the inexorable laws of physics. The first four planets, Mercury, Venus, Earth, Mars are earthlike, of solid material. The next four, Jupiter, Saturn, Uranus, Neptune, are much larger, gaseous, and the last, Pluto is large and rocklike, similar to an asteroid. All nine planets orbit the Sun counterclockwise and rotate counterclockwise (except Uranus and Venus) as does the Sun. All planetary satellites rotate counterclockwise except Neptune's Triton. The distance from the Sun of each planet's orbit increases with geometric regularity. The planetary orbits are in a plane around the Sun called the ecliptic, and their axis of rotation is roughly perpendicular to the ecliptic. The earth's axis varies 21° to 24° from perpendicular every 41,000 years. Uranus has the greatest tilt of all at 98 percent from perpendicular. A number of astronomers have suspected that Uranus' collision with an asteroid in the distant past caused this anomaly. An examination of those planets which can be observed shows multitudes of impact craters. The

Moon is a classic example. It has over 30,000 visible impact craters on its near side. More recent craters obliterate older ones, in whole or in part, making it impossible to estimate any impact totals or the last impact phase. The earth is a different matter. Being much larger than the Moon, it has suffered many more impacts but the evidence of this is not apparent to the eye. Only 200 impact craters are positively identified on earth. Very early on, the Moon lost its atmosphere. There are no oceans to hide craters and no agents of erosion (wind, water) to wear down existing craters. Earth still has its oceans and atmosphere. These forces have been at work for billions of years changing the features of the earth's crust. Were it not for this, the earth would look just like the Moon.

Were it not for plate tectonics and the erosive agents of wind and water, the earth would look exactly like the moon.

During the time of planet building (5.6 to 3.2 billion years B.P.), there were billions of planetary impacts. Since 3.2 billion years B.P., the rate has greatly slowed to the occasional strike of today. There has been no end to impacts, and we know a large impact would be catastrophic. What would be the most likely cause of such an impact? The answer of course is, an asteroid. Between Mars and Jupiter is located an "asteroid belt" containing tens of thousands of small planetary bodies revolving around the Sun. This total mass equals approximately $1/500$ of the mass of the earth. About a dozen have diameters of over 150 miles, about 500 have diameters of over 25 miles; the rest are much smaller. None are visible to the naked eye. The origin of the asteroids is a puzzle. It could well be a ring of primordial material that failed to form a planet. The asteroid belt is located exactly where, according to Bode's law, a planet should be. Perhaps at one time a planet did occupy this orbit and was destroyed by a collision. The former possibility is thought most likely. But, the asteroid belt is not a completely orderly thing. There are also thousands of asteroids whose orbits intersect the solar system that are not in the asteroid belt and their identification and orbit tracking is a severe challenge to astronomers. In 1962, only 1,647 asteroids had been assigned numbers and had well-determined orbits, even though it is estimated that the 100-inch Mt. Wilson telescope can detect 50,000 asteroids.

The asteroid belt is not in the ecliptic, the plane of the planets, rather it is inclined to it at 8.6°. The asteroid belt has a period of revolution around the Sun of 4.6 years. It moves counterclockwise, and its orbit is more elliptical than the planets'. The other non-belt asteroids often have extremely unusual orbits, presumably triggered by ancient collisions. In fact, the orbits of some asteroids have a common point of overlap causing astronomers to refer to the group as a "family." Scientists believe that *recent* asteroid collisions create "families."

Since we know that many asteroid orbits intersect the solar system close to Earth's orbit we would expect Earth to have some impacts and close calls. Earth has had both. That there were asteroid impacts on Earth early in the formation of the solar system we can assume, or prove, by looking at the Moon. Because Earth has been so environmentally active, specific asteroid impact points are hard to find. For instance, it was suggested in *Science,* Vol. 208, June 6, 1980, by Professor Alvarez and others, that an asteroid impact occurred at the Cretaceous-Tertiary boundary (65 million years ago) and caused the extinction of the dinosaurs. The clue to the impact is the presence of iridium in the CT soil structure of various points around the world. Rarely found on earth, iridium is a common component of extraterrestrial bodies. The article proposes that the asteroid was 6¼ miles in diameter; however, the crater has never been found. (The Chicxulub Crater on the north coast of the Yucatán Peninsula is now the prime suspect.) The authors state that three craters—over 100km (60 miles) and of appropriate age—are known on land but there is a two out of three chance that it, or any asteroid, fell in the ocean. There are the three possibilities: either the crater has been obliterated by erosion, subducted, or remains undiscovered.[33]

In historical times there has been no shortage of close calls by asteroids, which have thus served to remind man that space is a dangerous place and there is a great component of change in our continued existence. One family of seven asteroids, the Adonis group, seems to have a particular affinity for Earth. The orbits of all are quite extreme. They are very eccentric. The elliptical pattern is quite flattened. At perihelion, they come very close to the Sun and are inside the orbits of Venus, Earth, and Mars. At aphelion, the orbital curve farthest from the Sun, their orbits are beyond Jupiter and Saturn. All are about 6¼ miles in diameter, with a rocky crust but mostly consisting of a core of solid rock heavy with nickel, iron, and precious metals—an interstellar bullet composed of fabulously valuable minerals.[34] In 1931, Eros approached within 16,000,000 miles of Earth. In 1932, Apollo made a close approach. In 1936, Adonis came within 186,000 miles of Earth, considerably closer than the Moon (at 260,000 miles)—a very frightening close call. In fact, its orbit was slightly altered by the earth's gravitational pull; on October 10, 1937, Hermes passed only 600,000 miles away. Again, a very frightening pass. In 1968, Icarus passed 4,000,000 miles away. We are quite safe in saying that it was one of this group that hit the earth 10,500 years ago. Asteroids are the only interstellar objects that pose an immediate, catastrophic threat to the earth as a whole, but the earth is visited daily by a myriad of celestial bodies, some big and some small; minute particles enter the earth's atmosphere with an accumulated mass of 10,000 tons per day! Let us quickly review comets, meteors, and dust.

Comets are absolutely unique items. Spectacular, visible to the naked eye, radical in occurrence and orbit, they have long fascinated humans. They were regarded as portents for either good or evil, depending on what was desired and were frequently recorded. The Bayreuth tapestry is an excellent example of this, made to celebrate William, Duke of Normandy's victory over Edward II the Saxon King at Hastings, England in 1066. Halley's Comet is depicted as a favorable omen for William in his great military gamble. But comets are toothless tigers. They have great size but insignificant mass. The head of a comet ("coma") may be as large as the earth or Jupiter. Most comets have no tails, but some do, and this can be truly spectacular. Halley's Comet in 1910 had a tail of 90,000,000 miles (360 times the distance between the earth and Moon). It is thought that the head of a comet is composed of frozen gases, with some rock and metal particles. These ablate away to form the tail, which is so light it is pushed by the solar wind to a direction away from the Sun. Over eons of time, comets erode away and disappear. They are little threat to Earth.

Meteors are another story. Meteors, often seen as "shooting stars" are pieces of metal and/or rock that encounter Earth's atmosphere at astronomic speeds and upon being heated by friction become incandescent. The vast majority vaporize, but a few (called meteorites) reach the earth. The resulting impact will be directly proportional to its size. The average meteorite that does strike the ground probably weighs less than 200 pounds upon entering Earth's atmosphere, decreases in size due to burn off, slows down greatly because of atmospheric resistance and hits the earth with light enough impact to be found on the ground or immediately beneath it. About 2,000 such falls occur every year, but only about six are actually recovered. ("Falls" are observed meteorites and "finds" are found meteorites.) Worldwide, over 500 tons of meteorite material has been accumulated. Large meteorites can cause local disasters upon impact. On June 30, 1908, a meteorite, its flaming body visible in daylight, crashed to earth near the Tunguska River in Siberia. The fall was accompanied by large explosions; a great cloud of dust and smoke rose miles in the sky. The seismic event was recorded in Europe, and people were knocked down 100 miles away. Trees were flattened and burnt at a distance of up to 50 miles away. There were many craters some up to 150 feet in diameter. The bolide was estimated to weigh 50,000 tons. In February 1947, near Vladivostok, a meteorite struck creating an impact area 8 miles long and 3 miles wide with over 100 craters, a few more than 80 feet in diameter and 30 feet deep. A massive meteorite crater exists in the United States near Flagstaff, Arizona called the Barringer Meteor Crater. It is 4,200 feet in diameter with a lunarlike raised rim of 100 feet and a 600-feet deep crater. The rim is raised more on the south side, a clue that the meteorite approached from the north, and at a low angle. The crater is thought to be 75,000 years old.

Space dust is ubiquitous and comprises the 10,000 tons of minute particles that enter the earth's atmosphere daily. These particles have little or no velocity of their own, and because they are so small and so high there is almost no gravitational effect. They never produce a visible meteor, in fact, they never heat up as they have a large radiating surface compared to their volume. Nevertheless, the particles filter down eventually and are a significant component of raindrops. (Each drop requires a speck of solid matter upon which the water vapor condenses.) Space dust is an erosive agent to space vehicles. It is a good idea to contemplate the presence of space dust in and above Earth's atmosphere, because it provides a clue to a very pertinent question. After an asteroid collides with the earth, how long might dust from the impact affect the earth? The surprising answer is not weeks but thousands of years.

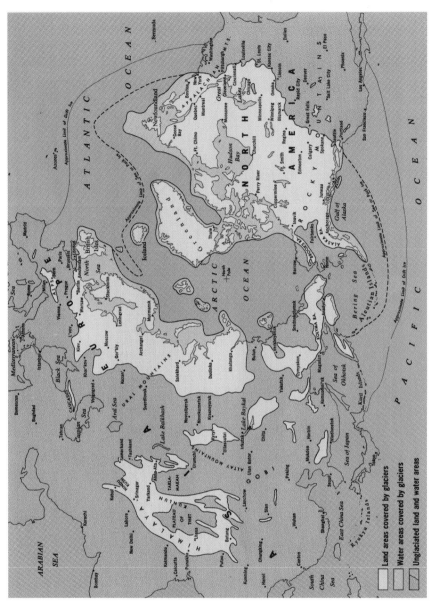

At glacial maximum 18,000 B.P., the world looked like this, but permafrost (not shown) was extensive. The earth was much colder and much drier. The Ice Age glaciers created the tropical deserts by causing aridity. *Hammond World Atlas Corporation*

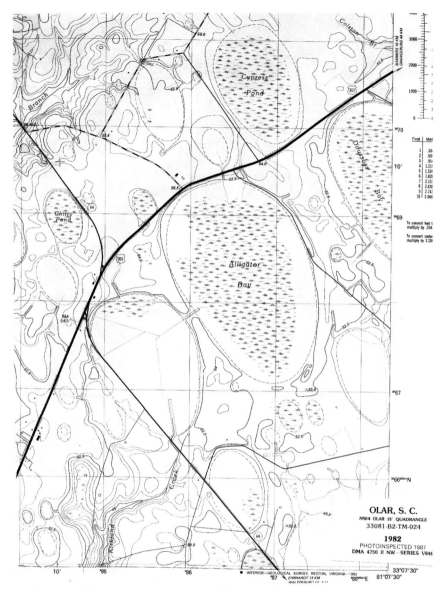

Map of a portion of the Carolina Bays. Compare to aerial photo on next page. *U.S. Geological Survey*

The aerial photo above, and the topographical map at left, clearly show portions of the Carolina Bays near Charleston, South Carolina. Now silted in, but still clearly visible, these boulder craters from the asteroid's crust point toward the impact crater in the Atlantic Ocean 1,500 miles away. *U.S. Geological Survey*

A brief study of the map shows how little land was left for man to occupy when one-third of the land was ice and permafrost, one-third was desert, and a good part of the remainder was mountains, hills, swamps, and jungle. Man used the ocean currents to find new places to live. *Hammond World Atlas Corporation*

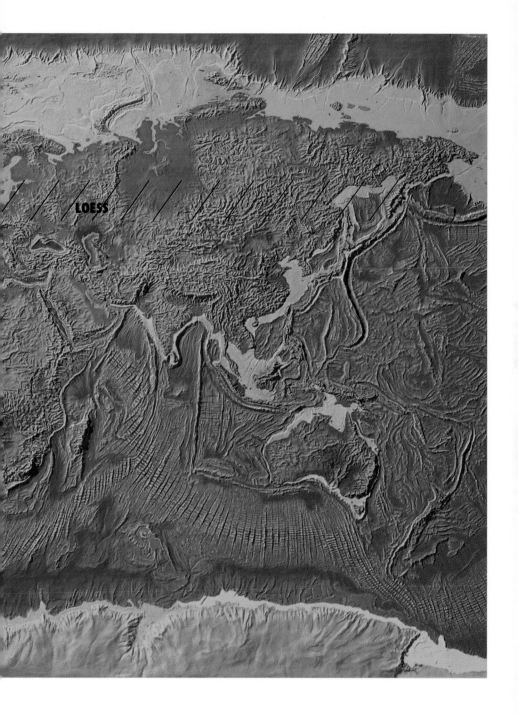

LOESS

Thor Heyerdahl's *Tigris*, the reed ship that sailed 4,300 miles was built with tools as simple as a knife and rope. This is the type of ship that helped populate the New World. *Carlo Mauri and the expedition crew*

The mummies of Arica, Chile carbon-date to 7810 B.P., three thousand years before the Egyptian civilization began. *Joe McNally*

This is the working camp in Greenland's arctic where scientists drilled the ice core that showed proof of the asteroid's impact at 10,500 B.P.: 1) the earth's rise in temperature; 2) trebbling of CO_2; 3) volcanic ash; and 4) sea salts. *Thomas Nebbia*

One that missed, but close! An asteroid of approximately 1,000 tons and 36 miles high going 40,000 miles per hour "skips" on the earth's atmosphere and continues into space. A fast-acting camper at Jackson Lake, Wyoming took this photograph on August 10, 1972. Had it hit earth, it would have had the force of an atomic bomb. *James M. Baker, Lillian, Alabama*

CHAPTER 17: THE ASTEROID IMPACT

At 10,500 B.P. the world changed forever. A great asteroid appeared in the sky south of Alaska, continued its flight over the world of ice and struck the earth in the Atlantic Ocean at 24°N latitude and 61°W longitude. Its flight was visible to man for about two minutes. The impact almost meant the end of the human race. The area of the North Atlantic is the most fragile part of the earth's crust, only 9 miles thick (continents are 20) and laced with fracture lines due to continental drift, the continuing separation of the American and European-African landmasses. All the fracture lines opened. All volcanoes came to life; one-tenth of the Atlantic went up into the atmosphere and came down as rain and mud from the ink black clouds, flooding all land downwind from the catastrophe. Heat, blast, lightning, asphyxiating gas, many feet of ash the consistency of liquid cement, and darkness completed the job. It was the end of the world.[35]

As the impact chronologically coincides with the end of the Ice Age, a number of astute thinkers have suspected that a great natural catastrophe occurred at this time, and a few of those have suspected an asteroid impact. Otto Muck most generously names Wyston, Count Carlin, de Lalande, Braghine, and Kelso de Montigny (an American anthropologist) as his predecessors. But that is modesty. All the credit goes to Otto Muck himself. It is Otto Muck who first suggested an asteroid strike at 65 million B.P. at the Cretaceous-Tertiary boundary (CT boundary), precisely at the time of the extinction of the dinosaurs. His evidence is continental drift. At 65 million years B.P., the southern tip of South America suddenly began to move to the east, evidence of a tremendous earth-shaking force. This continued until 10,500 B.P., when it changed course and began to drift westward, due to another massive earth-shaking force. This event, which occurred at 10,500 B.P. and caused the Patagonian drift pattern to reverse itself from east to west, was the impact in the North Atlantic Ocean of a second asteroid. It is the second asteroid impact we are concerned with and which we shall now address.

As previously stated, the asteroid that hit the earth at 10,500 B.P. was probably a member of the Adonis group, which particularly vexes the earth. It approached the earth in a very fast, flat trajectory, overtaking it. The asteroid probably would have barely missed Earth, as Adonis had in 1936; however, on the date of the impact there was a rare astronomical conjunction of Venus, Moon, and Earth which paralleled the asteroid's intersteller flight path and increased the gravitational pull toward Earth and bent its orbit just enough to cause it to collide, as hundreds of thousands of asteroids and meteorites have done before. Its speed was 43,000 miles per hour relative to Earth's. We are dealing with astronomical, that is, interplanetary speeds, nothing like anything to which we are accustomed. It approached the earth at a vertical angle of 30 degrees (to a pool player, a reflective shot). Like others of the Adonis group, it was 6¼ miles in diameter and of great mass composed of silica, nickel, and iron. It first became visible when it touched the earth's outer atmosphere at 250 miles elevation producing a red glow from hydrogen then becoming whiter due to the nitrogen-oxygen atmosphere, until it exceeded 36,000°F (20,000°C) and was twenty to one hundred times brighter than the Sun. Any creature that looked at it closely would be blinded. The elapsed time from its first appearance south of Alaska to its impact in the Atlantic Ocean was two minutes. It left a contrail like a modern high-flying airplane but with significant differences. It would appear as a streak of white smoke in the sky, coming up over the northwest horizon and going down through the southeast horizon. Its form was of billowing gas, and as the crust disintegrated and fell earthward, the particles slowed somewhat, but as the bolide was entirely on fire, it achieved a fantastic aspect which ancient man came to call the "feathered serpent." The whole apparition would have been huge in size, with the luminous gas trail smaller over the far horizon growing larger up to the white-hot head, which would equal the diameter of a full moon from the perspective of an onlooker 1,000 miles from its track. It could have been seen from 1,250 miles away, and every person on earth heard the core impact the Atlantic seabed. Just before the terrestrial impact, due to heat and tensile stress, the core burst in two with a tremendous explosion, nearly as loud as the impact, which immediately followed.

The path of the asteroid was from south of Alaska over Charleston, South Carolina to 24°N latitude and 61°W longitude in the North Atlantic, a clear-cut line. As the asteroid's crust disintegrated in its fall about 10,000 separate impacts occurred: 3,000 on land and 7,000 in the ocean. This is an unverified estimate. This explosion strip is an ellipse with its westerly curve surrounding Charleston, and its easterly end, 1,500 miles away is located at the two impact holes in the Atlantic seabed. The "Carolina Crater Field" became known in 1931 by accident through the then new medium of aerial photography. The craters had raised lips that pointed toward the southeast, silent but convincing evidence linking the two enormous sea holes 1,500 miles away. Even after 10,500 years of erosion and infilling these two sea holes are massive and unmistakable. Their size (77,000 square miles), depth (24,000 feet), and parallel half-circle shapes betray their non-geologic source. The whole explosion strip constitutes 63,500 square miles.

Before proceeding further, we must at this point stop and examine, just exactly what did this massive space traveler hit?

The earth is a sphere with an average circumference of 25,000 miles. It bulges slightly at the equator because of the gravitational pull of the Sun and the Moon, the same force that causes tides. It rotates once every 24 hours so it has a rotational speed of 1,000 miles per hour at the equator. This rotation, plus the effect of the radiant heat of the Sun, is the source of the energy that drives the currents in the earth's atmosphere and oceans. In one calendar year the earth makes a circuit around the Sun. The tilt of the earth's rotational axis causes the four seasons: The tilt toward the Sun in the Northern Hemisphere brings summer; the tilt away brings winter; at the "side" of the orbit where the Sun's rays strike the equator directly, comes spring and fall.[36]

The interior of the earth is composed of a core of liquid nickel-iron, a mantle composed of liquid magma (rock, metals, and gases) and a solid crust. The iron core is one-half of the earth's total diameter—7,900 miles. The mantle accounts for the rest except the crust; the earth's crust is solidified mantle averaging 20 miles thick under the continents and 9 miles thick under the oceans. Here we must note that the earth's crust "floats" on the mantle, which is very viscous, thus stabilizing the earth. However, given an appropriate impact this very thin crust can move independently of the mantle. The iron core represents one-third of the earth's mass, the mantle and crust two-thirds. The total mass of the earth is 6,595 (10^{18}) tons. Thus, we see that an asteroid of given mass, speed, and angle of incidence before impact is quite capable of moving the earth's crust (not in its entirety but along the line of the asteroid's flight path), not far perhaps, but devastating to every living thing on Earth. And, as the earth rotates, akin to a spinning top, the crust would "wobble" from such an impact, slowly returning to normal.

Man's knowledge of the interior properties of the earth largely stems from the Industrial Revolution (1850) to date. Measuring instruments, core drills, and inspired geologists and physicists have all contributed, but there is much to learn. The crust of the earth exists because of the cooling effect of the atmosphere. It is unnecessary and impossible to attempt a broad discussion of the crust's features. We must concentrate on one area, the Atlantic, particularly the North Atlantic where the asteroid hit. Our first goal is to describe the pertinent parts of the seafloor as a geologic entity. That is, to emphasize that like everything else in geology, it is not static. In fact, the very crust of the earth that lies above sea level and supports human life owes its origin to the magma activity below the seafloor. In the 1960s, oceanographers and geophysicists discovered that new seafloor is being created at the mid-oceanic ridges and slowly spreads away in opposite directions at the rate of 1 to 10 centimeters per year (the rate at which fingernails grow). Yet this force alone is responsible for mountain uplifting at the far edge of the tectonic plates. There are approximately a dozen of these plates. These forces are responsible for the existence of the Himalayas, the Cascades and Rocky Mountains, and the Andes. The same force also causes "subducting" of tectonic plates as in California and Japan, which in turn provides the world with an intimate view of the earth's infernal center as subducting causes volcanoes. The so-called "ring of fire" around the North Pacific Ocean includes on the east the Andes, Central America, the Cascades; and on the west the island arcs of the Aleutians, Japan, the Philippines (this list is not comprehensive). About one thousand active subduction volcanoes exist worldwide with forty erupting per year.[37] Thus, we see a corollary of plate tectonics—at the subduction end of plate tectonics there are volcanoes as evidence of the massive force of the submerged magma beneath the fragile crust of the earth.

Ocean ridges harbor active volcanoes, but few are observed. Only a small portion of the 43,000-mile Atlantic Ridge is above sea level (primarily Iceland); the rest lies below. Observing volcanic activity in Ice-

John Cogan

land provides great clues to undersea activity. We quickly find that *most* of the earth's volcanoes are hidden below the oceans; they exist by the hundreds on the great ocean ridges, a testament once again to the tenuous safety of the earth's crust. Fortunately, most of the volcanic activity associated with seafloor spreading from the oceanic ridges is "effusive." This means a gentle upwelling, spreading and crusting of the molten magma that forms uniquely shaped blocks called "pillow lava," which is one of the most common types of rock on earth, yet rarely observed by man, except where a rare occurrence has uplifted a seabed above sea level. Again, a testament to the thin gauze we call the earth's crust. But even this is marred. One glance at a bathometric map of the Atlantic Ocean shows countless fracture lines. These are true scars, healing lines, where in the process of seafloor spreading crustal stress caused fractures thousands of miles in length perpendicular to the mid-ocean ridge through which the magma effused then cooled and solidified. Fracture lines seem to represent a "slide" side by side of segments of the earth's crust. But the fracture seams are weak compared to the rock in between them and serve as a focus for the power of the magma beneath. What would be the fate of the earth if all of these fracture lines opened at once in the Atlantic? We will now address this question and others.

Our new subject is the force of the asteroid's impact. Before proceeding, a reminder is in order. We are *not* dealing with everyday terrestrial geophysical forces such as terrestrial speeds, gravity, caused falls, isolated volcanoes, hurricanes, thunderstorm clouds, or rivulets of magma. On the contrary, we are dealing with astronomical geophysical effects at first, and then reducing to terrestrial events of immediate effect, then to the lingering aftereffects of the asteroid impact.

The asteroid was first visible in the earth's atmosphere above the Gulf of Alaska. As it crossed North America in its descent, it was 20 to 100 times brighter than the sun. Every eye that was close to the flight path and looked directly at the asteroid would be blinded. It hit the North Atlantic with the force of 30,000 hydrogen bombs being detonated in one place. It penetrated the earth's crust (9 miles thick at the point of impact) to the liquid mantle, burning with a heat of 36,032°F (20,000°C). In multi-mini seconds the crust filled in behind it deflecting the blast effect sideways and deeper, breaking every fracture line from Iceland to Tristan da Cunha in the South Atlantic Ocean and igniting every volcano beneath the Atlantic Ocean. Possibly some of the nickel-iron core remained intact, probably most of it vaporized forming explosive gas that was the most direct cause of the crustal fracturing, which, in turn, explosively released thousands of cubic miles of magma into the Atlantic Ocean, causing one-tenth of the Atlantic to turn into superheated water vapor and rise into the earth's atmosphere to be carried by the prevailing winds all the way to Japan in the east and across Central America to the west.

As was previously discussed, the impact was powerful enough to make the earth wobble, and it did. Although we do not know the exact angle of the axis of the earth to the ecliptic during the Ice Age, we do know the angle now (23° 71') and we know it is now decreasing at 0.785' per century, on a curve, which indicates that the earth is recovering from an impact, which occurred 10,500 B.P. ago. Thus, we visualize the impact as causing submarine eruptions of the greatest possible violence, an impact that affected the revolution of the earth's crust and caused unimaginable terrestrial effects, which we will now discuss.

THE EXPLOSION STRIP The 6¼ mile in diameter asteroid entered the earth's atmosphere at 43,000 mph at a 30° angle of incidence to Earth at the point of impact and left a 1,500-mile explosion strip extending from Charleston, South Carolina (presently visible boulder impact craters) to the fractured cores' two craters at 61°W longitude 24°N latitude. The boulders so damaged the crust that to this day Charleston suffers tectonic earthquakes that occur in the area of the explosion strip. The cause is the spongelike character of the crustal substratum, which periodically collapses, a defect caused by the explosive force of the impacting boulders of the asteroid. Some 3,000 "Carolina Bays" or boulder impact craters exist on land and 7,000 undersea impacts are estimated to have occurred. Half of the bays are 1,300 feet long; over one hundred are a mile long. Most of the Carolina Bays are oval in shape. All of the longitudinal axes are parallel and most bays have an impact thrust wall to the southeast. This shows the northwest to southeast track of the asteroid. The size of the overall explosion strip, and the size of the two parallel impact craters readily lead to a calculation that the asteroid was approximately 6¼ miles in diameter upon entry into the earth's atmosphere. As we have seen, this is a common size. The two asteroid core craters on the seafloor of the Atlantic Ocean are 24,000 feet deep, approximately 140 miles in length, with a combined width of 70 miles.

TSUNAMIS The impact of the asteroid created immense tidal waves that repeatedly circled the world. They were hundreds of feet in height and scoured miles inland destroying and killing everything. Tsunamis or seismic sea waves travel 450 miles per hour or more in deep water, slow down in shallow water, dramatically increasing in height. Often, there is an outflow of water followed by the large vertical face of a wave with the highest water rising behind, rushing inland at great speed and dissipating as it spreads out. Earthquakes and undersea volcanic explosions have created tsunamis of 100 to 200 feet.[38] In 1703 at Awa, Japan a tsunami killed 100,000 people. The Krakatoa Island volcanic explosion of August 26, 27, 1883 created a tsunami of 115 feet (35 meters) and killed 36,000 people throughout the East Indies. An earthquake shook Lisbon, Portugal on November 1, 1775; an ensuing tsunami swept the city and 60,000 died. The tsunamis from the asteroid swept every shore, particularly the earth's central shores, and the tropics, where ice and aridity forced man to live.[39]

VOLCANISM The asteroid impact most probably produced the greatest volcanic event in the history of the earth. The impact of the core was the equivalent of the detonation of 30,000 hydrogen bombs at one place, and the place was deep beneath the crust of the earth in the North Atlantic which averages only 9 miles in thickness and is crossed by a number of fracture lines going east and west through the Atlantic Ridge ranging from Jan Mayan Island (in the Arctic north of Iceland) to Tristan da Cunha Island (mid-Atlantic even with Cape Town, South Africa). We can assume the nickel-iron core represented one-half of the asteroid's mass, and it hit (in two parts) at 43,000 miles per hour. It punched through the crust of the earth at an angle of 30° probably into the molten mantle; it was heated to vaporization with the explosive force directed down and sideways. The crust swelled over the affected area, probably 2,000 miles in radius, spontaneously rupturing all included fracture lines in that area and more, and starting the cracking process in all others as the volcanic explosions began and continued. All of the undersea volcanoes of the North Atlantic Ridge (over 200 are known) became active, including the five volcanoes of the nine islands of the Azores. All of Iceland's volcanoes became active as well, the only area of the Ridge now above sea level. Hundreds of unknown Atlantic Ridge volcanoes erupted.

Otto Muck quantifies the volcanic properties of the impact as follows: The Atlantic explosions lasted two to three days; the main fracture line area along the Atlantic Ridge was 2,480 miles long and averaged 78 miles wide giving an active volcanic area of 190,000 square miles; 560 to 480,000 cubic miles of magma exploded into the air with most blown away by the explosive force of the eruptions, inherent volcanic storms, and the prevailing winds. Thus, most of the magma did not fall back into the ocean; this loss of mantle caused the Atlantic seafloor to drop, resulting in a slope toward the point of the asteroid impact. In the area of the Azores, the drop was 2 to $2^{1}/2$ miles. The drop in the seafloor should not be shocking. Using the Azores as a reference point the gradient of seafloor depression is very slight: 500 to 1 (1,000 miles to the American continent; 1,000 to Europe; a 2-mile drop in seafloor).

Massive explosions continued for two to three days, the sound of which could be heard around the world.[40] The temperature of raw molten magma ranges from 900° to 1,800°. It is extremely viscous and contains great quantities of gas under enormous pressure. A commonplace volcanic vent is quite able to explode magma (which becomes pumice, ash, and dust) to the height of Mount Everest (29,000 feet). Contact with seawater greatly exacerbates the explosive effect of unplugged magma. The water will flash to steam and create a massive hydrothermal explosion—a steam blast (a unit of water heated to steam expands 1,672 times in volume). The rapid depressurization of magma magnifies the explosion. The gases are trapped in the magma until the last second when, being superheated, they explode just like an exploding steam boiler and expand to hundreds of times its volume in the molten rock in which it was dissolved under pressure. Explosiveness increases in proportion to the gas content of the magna. Gases comprise from .05 to 1.0 percent (by weight) of basalt magma and up to 5 to 6 percent of silica magma, and the Atlantic has both. Given Muck's estimate of 360,000 to 480,000 cubic miles of magma being blasted into the air over two to three days, we can readily see that the magma and gas produced would be enough to cover a continent.

ASPHYXIATING GASES The eruption of a cone-type volcano produces a common phenomenon, a pyroclastic flow. This is a high-speed (100 plus miles per hour) ash cloud, heavier than air, suffused with ash particles of flora and rock (picked up en route) and asphyxiating gas. These flows are high temperature, have great destructive force, and annihilate everything in their path. For instance, the Mount Pelee eruption in 1902 killed 30,000 inhabitants of San Pierre with pyroclastic flow. People on ships in the harbor (the few who survived) reported seeing the mountain erupt and the great dark cloud rush down the mountain across the city and out into the bay. It instantly set afire anything it touched and suffocated any living thing. Studies have been made of volcanic eruptions with pyroclastic flow, of gases emitted from fissure eruptions, and of isolated events such as the Lake Nyos, Cameroon gas cloud. The asphyxiating properties of volcanic gas are well understood. In the Lake Nyos disaster, a small deep lake filled a volcanic crater. Over many hundreds of years, volcanic gases (chiefly carbon dioxide) leaked up from the volcano, saturating the lower level of the lake. It is thought that cold, rainy weather caused the lake to "overturn," and the gas was released. On August 21, 1986, the deadly cloud heavier than air, flowed down the valley from the lake for 10 miles (16 kilometers) before it dissipated. It killed 2,000 people, 3,000 cattle, and all living creatures, even birds and flies. It was an absolute extinction of life. Had the volcano erupted, the carnage would have been much worse as the asphyxiating gas would have been spread over a greater area, diluted but still deadly.

Volcanic gases are composed of roughly 43 percent carbon dioxide, 26 percent nitrogen, 27 percent water vapor, sulfur dioxide, and other gases are 4 percent. Carbon dioxide, hydrogen sulfide, chloride, and other highly volatile compounds are the main killers as they expand to cover vast distances; their heat and toxicity are lethal to all living things. (Carbon dioxide is not toxic, but a sustained atmosphere of 5 percent CO_2 is fatal to humans.) The volcanic gas is dissolved in the magma while it is at rest. Upon release of the magma by volcanic eruption, the gas separates explosively, expanding to hundreds of times its volume in the magma in which it was contained under pressure. As previously noted, the Atlantic catastrophe combined steam from the Atlantic Ocean and volcanic gases, plus the solid material of the ocean floor and the erupting magma. The gas produced a continent-sized cloud.

Other volcanic gases are destructive and lethal but in quite a different way. These are of the Freon type (chlorofluorocarbons) and chlorine, and exist in sufficient quantity in the magma (amply provided by the Atlantic catastrophe) to eliminate the ozone layer that protects the earth. This layer, which extends from 12 to 30 miles above earth, absorbs the shortwave ultraviolet radiation of the Sun. This radiation can do extreme genetic damage to humans and all living things. In fact it did, but let us reserve discussion of this subject until "Chapter 19: The Great Extinction."

RAIN AND ASH Muck estimates that from 360,000 to 480,000 cubic miles of magma violently erupted into the atmosphere as a result of the fracturing of the Atlantic seabed. Some fell back into the sea; most of the magma became fly ash and dust, eventually distributed world-wide by the wind. Given that amount of magma hurled to great heights by steam—water vapor—a massive amount of water was required, about 4,800,000 cubic miles of water or one-tenth of the water volume of the North Atlantic Ocean ($^1/_{120}$ of all seawater). The loss of this water caused the sea level to drop about 130 feet over the Atlantic Ridge, the focal point of the volcanic eruptions. This, in turn, created massive currents in the Atlantic; surface currents rushed toward the Ridge, collided and rebounded causing the massive tsunamis that devastated the world's shorelines; as the Ridge sank and the volcanism continued, deep-ocean currents deposited their accumulated seafloor sediment in the valleys along the Ridge.

That much fly ash and water vapor cooling and condensing into water provides a formidable portent of rain mixed with ash, a suffocating atmosphere, and a deadly deposit of mud crushing everything. This would continue for the two to three days of the Atlantic eruptions, and weeks thereafter as the great continental size cloud continued to spread. Otto Muck estimates the mean depth of rainfall across Eurasia to be about 100 feet; to carry this much water, the cloud would have to have a mean height of 18.5 miles (30km) or three times higher than Mount Everest.

Air currents affected the spread of the massive ash cloud. Once a particle is airborne it is utterly influenced by the prevailing wind. It goes where the wind goes and nowhere else. Along the equator, north and south of it, the trade winds flow from east to west, but more northerly, the wind flows from west to east. Thus, the cloud was divided with one-third carried by the trade winds to the west and two-thirds by the more northerly winds blowing in the opposite direction, to the east.

The recent eruption of Mount St. Helens on May 18, 1980 in Washington State provides a graphic example of the statements made above. Given the eruption of a cone-type volcano one might expect the ash to fall in a 360-degree circle around the mountain. Nothing of the sort happened. The prevailing wind blew the ash from west to east along a clearly defined path. Citizens of Portland, Oregon and Seattle, Washington watched the eruption with awe, but only the populace of eastern Washington, northern Idaho, and part of Montana were in the wind's path and suffered the fall of ash. The ash was heavy. Dry ash on a 2,500-square-foot rooftop weighed 15,000 pounds. When wet, it would weigh twice as much.

If we look at the Atlantic catastrophe we see that the same thing happened. The eastward winds blew the ink black cloud of ash from the Atlantic to China and Siberia. The ash left a trail: loess, now weathered volcanic ash, the most fertile soil in the world, and it lies in a perfectly defined belt, characteristic of the wind flow at about 40° plus latitude. The loess is magma, fly ash, mixed with the Atlantic seafloor, the accumulation of billions of years of calcareous marine ooze. Loess is hundreds of feet deep in places. It is rich in calcium, nitrates, phosphates, mineral salts, and trace elements because of its volcanic and marine origin. It does not require fertilizer to produce abundant crops.

The ink black cloud that traveled west to east across Eurasia was appalling to see and fatal to be enveloped in. It was black—so thick a lantern could not be seen at arms' length and superheated (over 1,000°F). For days it set fire to everything in its path. Yet, anomalously, what it did not burn it drowned with water and buried in ash. There were constant lightning bolts caused by static electricity created by the fly ash. These generated loud thunderclaps heard hundreds of miles away. The winds within the cloud created by the expanding gas exceeded anything ever experienced on earth. (Hurricanes reach 200 miles per hour; tornadoes have been estimated at 800 miles per hour.) These forces were so strong that millions of large animals in Siberia were physically ripped apart. Mud and rain water placed them in piles, where their disarticulated bones are to be found to this day. The cloud displaced the normal atmosphere and its gases asphyxiated all that came within it. Anything that survived had to be outside the cloud's path, and that would depend entirely upon the prevailing winds.

DUST CLOUDS Given a volcanic eruption the detritus will fall to earth in a marked order: large material (rocks, gravel, pumice stone); medium material (large sand, finer sand); fine material (fly ash which is not really ash at all but rather a very special form of volcanic glass); and the finest material of all, dust. The dust, however, will spend a great deal of time in the atmosphere before returning to earth; how long will depend on various imponderables, such as: exactly how fine the particles are (for example, basaltic versus rhyolite or other magma, the former causing finer particles), and how far it is blasted upward. Very fine particles of dust (about one micron or 0.001 millimeter in diameter) from a particularly violent eruption have often found their way into the stratosphere where they move with the jet streams and encircle the earth, remaining there for years. Two recently observed eruptions provide examples of this. Krakatoa's eruption in 1883 produced a high-altitude haze layer that encircled the earth and produced magnificent visual effects at sunset. The color of the sunset haze changed from green, to orange, to deep scarlet, slowly sinking in the west as the stars appeared. Twilight, usually thirty minutes lasted ninety minutes. This haze layer was estimated to be 31 miles high (50km) and lasted several years giving scientists the first clear signal that volcanic eruptions can affect the entire planet. Mount El Chichon in southern Mexico on March 28, 1982, blasted gases and ash 12.5 miles (20km) into the sky. The eruptions continued for eight days and formed a cloud that trade winds blew directly west almost in a straight line. It reached Hawaii in six days, Japan in nineteen days, and had circled the earth in thirty days, in a very narrow band determined by the trade winds. After several years of atmospheric mixing, it was gone.

Volcanic dust remains aloft for years for a very good reason—lack of gravitational force. Let us imagine a volcanic dust cloud 50 miles high (80 km). One dust particle has only infinitesimal mass and Earth's gravitational force is inversely proportional to the square of the distance (center to center) between the bodies. Thus, given a dust cloud well into the stratosphere, the higher it is, the longer it will stay.

These clouds are creatures of the wind. Given a massive volcanic eruption in the Northern Hemisphere it would be almost impossible for the dust cloud to expand to the Southern Hemisphere because of the east to west trade winds on both sides of the equator. Jet streams follow particular paths as well but always roughly parallel with the equator, never crossing it. And there is a force at work that would directly counter any movement toward the Southern Hemisphere by a volcanic dust cloud in the Northern Hemisphere, the Coriolis effect. The earth rotates around its axis most rapidly at the equator, its speed of rotation diminishing in proportion to the distance north (1,000 miles per hour at the equator, 500 miles per hour at 45°N latitude, 0 miles per hour at the North Pole). Thus, the north equatorial trade wind has a tendency to bleed off toward the area of slower rotation, that is, to the north. In the Southern Hemisphere, exactly the same thing happens, in reverse.

John Cogan

The Coriolis effect plus the jet streams caused the great death cloud to compound northward, toward the upper latitudes, even the polar area itself. It would take a cloud of this nature from one to two thousand years to dissipate. The picture then, is of the dust cloud, continental in size and of immense height, gradually moving northward, continually rising, and dissipating over a period of one to two thousand years. This towering, immense continental size cloud in the north, shimmering in the sunlight, must have been seen from afar by the greatly reduced number of humans and animals that survived the asteroid impact. Only 5 to 10 percent of the sunlight reached the earth during the first thousand years under the thickest parts of the cloud, increasing in amount gradually over the next thousand(s?) years. The immense cloud floated above the earth, its base very high, from 124 to 186 miles (200 to 300km) and its top 62 miles (100km) above that; it extended from the North Pole to 50° latitude, the United States-Canadian border, and could be seen from 1,250 miles farther south. To an observer in the south it would look bright, subtly changing, akin in appearance to a high mountain range on the horizon, forty times higher than the Himalayas. Is this exaggeration? Not at all. We have recorded volcanic eruptions that will serve as the basis for an estimate. The asteroid impact caused a volcanic eruption twenty thousand times greater than the Krakatoa eruption of 1883 which blew 50 miles high and created a reflective shield of dust particles that lasted thirteen years and which for three years after the explosion caused a 10 percent reduction of solar radiation reaching the earth's surface at Montpellier, France—halfway around the world. The eruption of Mount Tambora in 1815 caused the disastrous New England crop failures of 1816, produced the coldest summer in Geneva, Switzerland in sixty years, and dropped the entire world's temperature 2° below normal for a year. The 1963 volcanic eruption on Bali caused a drop in solar radiation at Pretoria, South Africa of 5 percent. Volcanic activity produces a worldwide effect in the weather because of the dust cloud.

PUMICE STONE A great portion of the magma erupted from the Atlantic basin formed pumice stone, a very light spongelike rock filled with air or gas bubble holes. It is caused by the violent eruption of magma, thick with water vapor, which expands as the pressure of the containing earth is instantly reduced to normal atmospheric pressure. It is, however, exactly the same material as fly ash. The pumice stones, seldom as large as a basketball, come from a less violent part of the eruption—its edge, and are not carried far by the violent winds. It will fall to the earth's surface near the point of eruption; if it falls into the ocean, it will float. It will float for years as only friction between the pumice particles caused by waves will abrade it; the slow waterlogging of the stone in contact with the seawater will cause it to sink. The Krakatoa explosion of 1883 produced a layer of pumice stone (specific gravity 0.5), 10 inches thick (25.4cm) over a radius of 310 miles (500km) for a total area of 290,000 square miles (750,000sq km). It stopped small boat traffic and hindered large shipping for several months. The asteroid impact by comparison, using the Krakatoa eruption as a measure, covered the Atlantic to a height of 330 feet in the mid-North Atlantic, slowly dissipated and finally disappeared after 3,000 years.

THE EARTH WOBBLES It is very easy to do an Einstein "thought experiment" at this point. Imagine the spinning Earth, a small planet, held in place in its orbit around the Sun by Newton's law of gravity. Imagine an asteroid $6^{1}/_{4}$ miles (10km) in diameter approaching from "behind" and overtaking the earth at a speed of 43,000 miles per hour; the asteroid hits the surface of the earth at an angle of 30° to the surface of the earth and disappears straight ahead into the crust of the earth and the mantle to explode and vaporize. Will the earth move? The core of the earth itself will not move as its mass is too great, but the crust of the earth can move on the liquid magma. The axis of rotation will change or "move" on an exact line from its former position toward the point of impact of the asteroid, just like a child's spinning top does when flicked with a finger. In fact, the asteroid caused a movement of the earth's axis of rotation of about 2°. The crust moved an estimated 2,100 miles (3,400km) along the line of the flight path of the asteroid. North America moved toward the equator; Siberia moved away from the equator, northward. The Sun's rays remained the same, but the earth's weather changed, warming North America and freezing Siberia. During the Ice Age, the axis of rotation was more vertical, thus there was less extremity in the seasons *before* the asteroid impact than *after* it; this was a significant factor in ending the Ice Age. This effect of the asteroid impact is, however, very difficult to prove and will be discussed further in "Chapter 24: Speculation and Comment."

CHAPTER 18: THE HEALING EARTH

Since the asteroid hit earth 10,500 years have passed. Its impact was contemporaneous with the end of the Ice Age, and this unfortunate fact has masked the reality of the event from scientists and academicians of today. But that will soon end, as there is plenty of residual evidence of the event left in the healing earth. Also, several great "mysteries of science" are not mysteries at all. For instance, the asteroid impact was the cause of death for numerous species of megafauna (large animals) of North and South America, Eurasia, and Australia. We will discuss exactly how it happened in the next chapter.

One of the greatest clues to the reality of the asteroid impact are the Greenland ice cores. The scientific text from *Quaternary Environments* discusses the cores in detail. These cores can be dated at given levels by counting the annual layers (much like tree rings). Cores 1.24 miles (2km) deep have been taken which represent in time 160,000 years or before the last interglacial period prior to the last advance of the ice. But, what do the cores show regarding the condition of Greenland 10,500 years ago? The core from Camp Century at 77°N in northern Greenland at 3,773 feet deep (1,150 meters), shows four geophysical phenomena that simultaneously and instantaneously occurred at 10,500 B.P., and can only be explained by the asteroid impact. These phenomena are: first, a large rise in temperature of the earth's atmosphere; second, an increase of three times the amount of carbon dioxide in the earth's atmosphere; third, the deposit of atmospheric dust composed of volcanic ash and clay particles; and fourth, the deposit of airborne sea salt.

ATMOSPHERIC WARMING Immediately after the asteroid impact, the earth's atmosphere warmed by 20°F (11°C). (This measurement was made by using certain oxygen isotopes.) Geophysical science has never before witnessed such an event and the highly scientific authors of

Quaternary Environments engage in uncharacteristic exuberance using an exclamation point to express emotion seldom seen in scientific papers: "the transition is reflected in only 2m (6.5 feet) of ice, which corresponds to only about 100 years!" The warming continued to 9,000 B.P. when it reached today's levels. All science accepts the 10,500 B.P. date as the mark of the transition from the Ice Age, the Pleistocene, to the modern age, the Holocene. But only the ice core itself could prove that the atmospheric temperature change was instantaneous. The ocean also abruptly warmed by several degrees at this time, as proved by the examination of seashells by Lamont Observatory scientists. The fast retreat of the glaciers began at this time. Thus, the evidence of both land and sea comport with the record of abrupt warming as shown by the ice core. The abrupt warming was caused primarily by the release of massive amounts of carbon dioxide into the earth's atmosphere as a result of the Atlantic eruptions, which we now address.

CARBON DIOXIDE The core shows an instantaneous increase of three times the normal amount of carbon dioxide in the earth's atmosphere. This is very surprising as the Ice Age was dry, cold and the atmosphere was deficient in carbon dioxide. The question is: What could possibly be the *source* of such a massive amount of carbon dioxide? The answer is straightforward: The asteroid impact caused the release of this amount of carbon dioxide into the atmosphere through volcanic action; its source was carbon dioxide gas dissolved in both the erupted mantle and the deep-ocean seawater. The first source of carbon dioxide was from the magma, which was released by the eruptions. Each unit of gas upon release from the magma expanded to hundreds of times its former volume. The second and greater amount came from the depths of the Atlantic Ocean, the only possible source for this much carbon dioxide. The oceans hold 95 percent of the earth's carbon dioxide, most of it in solution with seawater in the deepest parts of the oceans—only releasable by cataclysmic undersea volcanic eruptions. And given such an event, and the release of enough carbon dioxide so as to triple the amount in the earth's atmosphere, the atmosphere will become instantly warmer. The earth receives incoming shortwave solar radiation, which passes through the atmosphere and warms the earth. The earth then radiates longwave radiation as heat, one-third of which is absorbed by gases in the atmosphere and is slowly remitted. Water vapor and carbon dioxide trap 42 percent of this retained heat. Carbon dioxide is far more efficient as a heat trap than water vapor. Representing only .03 percent of the volume of the normal atmosphere, carbon dioxide traps 15 percent of the earth's radiated heat. If all carbon dioxide were eliminated from the earth's atmosphere, the average temperature of the earth would drop to 27°F (–2.78°C). The immediate temperature rise caused by the vast increase in carbon dioxide in the earth's atmosphere after the asteroid impact was later followed by a drop in the earth's temperature as the water vapor and carbon dioxide dissipated. However, the very fine dust particles still remained aloft in the circling remains of the great death cloud and reflected the Sun's incoming rays back into space. It is good that it did. Otherwise, the rapid melt of the ice sheets, which took 4,000 years, would have been much faster. As it was, the melt flooded Canada and much of the United States, but it drained into the oceans in sufficient time to cause the reemerging land to be healthy and fertile. Had the melt been faster the land would have become brackish and muskeg like.

ATMOSPHERIC DUST Greenland, having no dust of its own, almost at the North Pole and thousands of miles from the nearest possible source of the dust and so far north it is out of any wind pattern, could only receive dust composed of volcanic ash and clay particles (from the Atlantic Ocean seabed) from a massive volcanic event on a scale thousands of times greater than any known eruption which must have caused atmospheric dust to permeate the atmosphere of the entire Northern Hemisphere.

SEA SALTS When ocean water evaporates under normal conditions, the salt remains in the sea and clean water vapor enters the atmosphere. Only massive submarine volcanic eruptions could produce this amount of sea salt in the atmosphere over Greenland. The ice core also showed that the concentration of atmospheric sea salts fell by 75 percent in less than one hundred years, thereby proving that the event causing the sea salt to be in the atmosphere was a single happening from which the earth recovered.

Thus, the Greenland ice cores neatly sum up the effect of the asteroid impact: a very rapid increase in temperature on land and water; fallout of dust, mostly volcanic ash and some clay indicating a turbulent and dirty atmosphere which for the only time in the earth's history during the Ice Age contained a vast amount of sea salts; and the sudden tripling of carbon dioxide in the atmosphere. All of this is perfect evidence of the great dust cloud, continental in size, created by the asteroid's impact. It is a very clear record and having obtained it only in the last few years, we are fortunate to have it. Greenland, far north and out of the prevailing winds, was barely on the edge of the Atlantic catastrophe. And to cap the point: the Antarctic ice cores of 10,500 B.P. are vastly cleaner. Exactly what one would expect as very little of the eruptive detritus from the Atlantic eruptions reached the South Pole.

The loess belt or "black earth belt" is a fabulous relic of the Atlantic eruptions. Now 10,500 years old, the soil is so rich it still does not require fertilizer. Its calcium and chalk components come from marine sediments; its quartz comes from erupting magma. The belt itself, extending from Europe to China is a perfect track of the prevailing wind at the time of the asteroid impact. It covers 5 to10 percent of the Eurasian land area (4,000,000 to 8,000,000 square miles or 10,000,000 to 20,000,000 square kilometers) to an average depth of 330 feet (100 meters). Scientists are utterly baffled about its origin. The only theory of significance advanced so far to explain it is the Aeolian theory that in effect says that it is the product of dust blown by the wind from recently unglaciated ground. However, this theory completely fails:

1. Along the 5,000-mile track of the loess belt there were no glaciers to provide its source.

2. No mountain ranges exist that are rich in calcium nor is there any other source of calcium which was in fact supplied by the marine ooze.

3. Loess also contains a large amount of quicklime which requires heat for its production, which in fact was produced by the volcanic eruption—impossible on a frigid steppe.

4. In China, the loess is evenly deposited on steep mountains. If normal winds provided the transport of the loess, the mountains would clearly reflect this by appropriate dunes and eddies. The picture is quite different. This material came straight down, falling equally in all places. It is clearly the product of a deluge, not of wind.[41]

The North Atlantic fracture lines have healed, and the asteroid crater holes have silted in, although they are still 24,000 feet deep. But the ocean still bears evidence of the rapid drop of its seabed. Disparate evidence comes together that satisfactorily proves the North Atlantic Ridge suddenly submerged at the end of the Ice Age.

1. Fridtjof Nansen from 1883 to 1896 found that in the seabed between Iceland and Scotland large quantities of shallow water seashells were found, at a depth of up to 8,200 feet (2,500 meters) indicating a sudden drop of 6,500 feet (2,000 meters) of the seafloor in that area. A gradient sloping from north to south was noted.

2. In 1913 Paul Termier, director of the French Oceanographic Institute, gave a lecture regarding a tachylite rock taken from the Azores Plateau in 1898 during the laying of the transatlantic telephone cable. He declared the rock to be of volcanic origin; it had solidified in air, not water. It still had sharp edges, and as tachylite dissolves rapidly in seawater as it was of recent origin—approximately 10,500 B.P.

3. The Piggott cores from the North Atlantic in the 1930s contain volcanic ash at the 10,500 B.P. level indicating massive volcanic action in that area. The core from the Azores plateau had only 3¹/₈ inches of sedimentary material indicating the plateau had subsided only 10,500 years before.

4. In 1947, the Swedish ship *Albatross* working in the Azores, produced sea cores containing freshwater algae from 12,000 feet deep.

5. The underwater profile of the rocks of the Azores Mountains shows they are sharp, therefore, newly submerged. This sharpness of the underwater rocks of the Azores is visible to divers and perhaps to American and Russian submarines that scoot through the area playing deadly games. If the Azores had been submerged for eons these rocks would be blunted, rounded off by chemical and mechanical forces; however, if the submergence occurred only 10,500 years ago then the rocks would have, as they do, a sharp profile.

6. When we compare the seabed of the Atlantic to that of the Pacific we find a difference. "A large part of the Atlantic basin is covered by acid *volcanic magma* of *recent origin*. In contrast, the Pacific, though scarcely less active consists of paleogenous (that is old, ancient) basic magma." (italics added for empha-

sis) Otto Muck, *The Secret of Atlantis*, p. 147.

Given an event of the magnitude of the asteroid impact shouldn't there be some special evidence of this on the Atlantic seafloor? It would seem this should be true and upon investigation we find it is true. Seafloor sediments tell the tale. The impact caused two to three days of eruptions along the North Atlantic Ridge that sank 10,000 feet as the magma was expelled and one-tenth of the Atlantic Ocean blasted into the atmosphere. This would cause ocean currents to form directed toward the Atlantic Ridge. The currents would pick up sediments on the seafloor along with eruptive material and this material should be deposited about the undersea mountains of the ridge. As the volcanic event came to an end the eruptions would cease and the currents would abate. Upon investigation we find precise evidence of such sediment deposit. In the book *The Sea Around Us*, Rachel Carson describes the sediment finds in the North Atlantic and especially along the Atlantic Ridge made by the Swedish Deep Sea Expedition from 1947 to 1948 aboard the ship *Albatross* which took many deep-sea cores and used explosives for seismic effect to measure the thickness of sediment. (Also to be noted are the efforts of Professor W. Maurice Ewing and the Woods Hole Oceanographic Institute whose ship *Atlantis* did similar work, especially around the Azores at about the same time). Carson states:

> Over vast areas of the Pacific the average thickness of the sediments (unconsolidated sediments plus sedimentary rock) is only about a quarter of a mile. It is a little thicker over much of the Atlantic. (p. 203) ... most people felt a shock of surprise and wonder when Hans Pettersson, leader of the Swedish Deep Sea Expedition, announced that the *Albatross* measurements taken in the open Atlantic Basin showed sediment layers as much as 12,000 feet thick. (p. 79) ... Interesting variations in the thickness of the sediment layer of the Atlantic Ridge and the approaches to the Ridge from the American side were reported by Ewing. As the bottom contours became less even and began to slope up into the foothills of the Ridge, the sediments thickened, as though piling up into mammoth drifts 1,000 to 2,000 feet deep against the slopes of the hills. Farther up in the mountains of the Ridge, where there are many level terraces from a few to a score of miles wide, the sediments were even deeper, measuring up to

John Cogan

3,000 feet. But along the backbone of the Ridge, on the steep slopes and peaks and pinnacles, the bare rock emerged, swept clean of sediments. (p. 80)

It is a well-described picture of the deposit of sediments, partly from the ocean floor and partly from the eruption material that fell into the North Atlantic. These sedimentary deposits were moved by the ocean currents created by the sinking of the ocean floor, by volcanic eruptions that blasted one-tenth of the Atlantic Ocean into the atmosphere, and the consequent temporary lowering of the ocean water level at the Mid-Atlantic Ridge. These currents would be drawn toward the Atlantic Ridge eruptions just as water is drawn toward a drain in the bathtub. This obvious proof of the massive ocean currents associated with the impact and subsequent eruptions explains another phenomenon that occurred at that time—the release of massive amounts of carbon dioxide into the earth's atmosphere. Deep-ocean currents caused its release by transporting the dissolved gas and its containing seawater to the submarine volcanic eruptions where it was expelled into the atmosphere.

The Atlantic has changed, given the twin impetus of the end of the Ice Age and the asteroid strike. The first major phenomenon is the rise in sea level of 400 feet. The period of maximum glaciations, the height of the Ice Age, was reached at 18,000 B.P.; but the period 18,000 to 10,500 B.P. could be characterized as static, and the melting of the great ice sheets did not begin with rapidity until the asteroid strike. The asteroid strike produced an instant and substantial warming of the earth, and the great ice sheets began to melt. As the great explosion cloud disappeared, the melting of the remaining ice quickened until its present location was reached about 6500 B.P. The oceans rose about 400 feet over these 4,000 years from the addition of the meltwater. The abrupt subsidence of the Atlantic seafloor produced a second phenomenon—the Gulf Stream now reached Europe. During the Ice Age this great river of warm water (sometimes 20°F warmer than the North Atlantic itself), larger than all the rivers of the world combined, moved at a rate of five miles per hour from the South Atlantic to the Caribbean, along the eastern seacoast of North America, northeast to the Azores (then a huge island platform the size of Spain), southeasterly to mix with the waters of Africa forming the start of the current. Were it not for the fact that the Azores platform blocked the Gulf Stream, Europe could not possibly have become glaciated as it did; the Gulf Stream would have prevented that. The Europe of today owes its beneficial climate entirely to the Gulf Stream; otherwise, it would have a climate comparable to other geographical areas of its latitude such as Labrador, southeast Alaska, southern Siberia. The Azores platform sank because of the asteroid strike and for no other reason. The Gulf Stream brought warm water, warm temperatures and rain to Europe. After the Gulf Stream arrived in Europe and glaciers retreated, Europe became one of the most attractive places on earth for human habitat.

CHAPTER 19: THE GREAT EXTINCTION

At the end of the Ice Age at 10,500 B.P., a mass extinction of well over half of the existing species of megafauna (large animals) occurred throughout the world. The asteroid impact caused the loss of these animals. The extinction had nothing to do with glaciations, weather, natural conditions of any kind, or as has been absurdly suggested, overhunting by humans. It was stated earlier that the end of the Ice Age served to mask the fact of the asteroid impact. Nowhere is this more pertinent than in the matter of the megafuna extinction. Modern science rates the extinction of these animals as one of the great unsolved mysteries of science. And well it should be. Until the asteroid impact is factored in, the cause of the extinction is unsolvable.

The Ice Age was a wonderful time for the existence of mammals. A great diversity of species inhabited the earth in prolific numbers. Because of the earth's colder temperature overall, especially near the ice, many developed massive bodies; large bodies offer better protection from cold. These animals were well adapted to the conditions and had lived successfully for millions of years, their heritage going back 60 million years to the time of the demise of the dinosaurs. Yet, within a few hundred years after 10,500 B.P., well over half of the megafauna species of the earth were gone. The asteroid's impact did two things to the viability of megafauna life on earth. First, the massive volcanic activity of the impact killed millions of these animals outright (over 50 million); second, it allowed hard radiation to reach the earth causing the widespread extinctions.

Let us examine the mass death of animals caused by the asteroid's impact. One animal, the woolly mammoth, requires our focus because of its majesty. Incredibly, preservation by freezing has made many specimens available to us for study, bringing it into our world. There are two kinds of mammoths: the woolly mammoth of Eurasia, and the Colombian or Imperial mammoth of North America, which lived south of the ice sheet and was 10 percent larger than the woolly. Mammoths are closely related to the elephant and originated in Africa about four million years ago, thereafter, migrating outward. From 750,000 to 500,000 years ago the ancestral steppe mammoth had a worldwide range in the upper Northern Hemisphere and through adaptation to the Ice Ages by 250,000 years ago it became the woolly mammoth. By 10,500 B.P., the woolly's range was from England to Alaska. There were perhaps 40 million mammoths; there were nearly as many in number as the bison on the North American Great Plains when first seen by Europeans.

The woolly mammoths of Siberia were almost fantastic creatures that developed the most cold-weather efficient body form on earth. Large bodies retain heat well, and large they were. Thirteen feet high, 15 feet long, tusks 8 feet long (both male and female), a trunk 6 feet long, huge legs 1$^1/_2$ feet thick, weight 6 to 7 tons. Its adaptation to cold was complete; a way of saying that it was a highly specialized animal. It had dense undercoats of softer hair, woollike, warm, thick and brown colored. About the shoulders and back it had a manelike ruff of stiff hair, 12 to 14 inches long and deep brown in color, with a distinct reddish tint. The skin on the back of a cold-weather animal is always much thicker than the belly. The mammoths' shoulder skin could be 1 inch thick; underneath was a layer of fat, 3 to 4 inches thick. It had pronounced humps on its head and shoulders that provided a fat reserve. The extremities were small (ears, feet, tail, trunk) for the animal's size, a cold-weather adaptation. The teeth were extremely tough, with numerous hard, close-set ridges, allowing them to chew course vegetation. A mammoth matured slowly, a young bull leaving the cow-calf herd at about twenty years of age, and probably lived the same life span as a wild elephant of today, sixty to eighty years. A popular misconception is that the woolly mammoth lived in an environment of ice and snow. On the contrary, their habitat was cold but temperate enough to produce bountiful food. There was no permafrost then, but the climate has changed since 10,500 B.P. from temperate to arctic thereby creating the permafrost in which the mammoths are entombed. The original mammoth habitat is often referred to as the "mammoth steppe" somewhat different from any existing habitat today. It consisted of great amounts of grass, shrubs, arctic sagebrush, many herbaceous plants, and intermittent fir and pine forests.

The mix was needed to obtain all the proper nutrients. An adult mammoth would feed for up to twenty hours per day and ingest 400 pounds of food and defecate 200 pounds a day. The mammoths plus the millions of other grazing animals (such as the woolly rhino, bison, horses, reindeer, musk ox, moose, giant elk) extracted thousands of tons of food daily from this grazing paradise which today is nutrient-deficient tundra growing on permafrost and supports very few animals. (This was a land of low vegetation and no shade). The stomach contents of a mammoth were well described in an 1846 letter by Mr. Benkendorf to a German friend. Near the mouth of the Indigirka River, on the Arctic Ocean, Benkendorf's survey party roped and landed a semi-submerged mammoth carcass found floating in the river during the spring flood. Its hindquarters were still in the submerged bank's permafrost; the men had to wait while the river finally eroded it free. They had a short time to work on the mammoth. Unfortunately, the river undermined the bank, nearly drowned the men and swept the carcass away. Part of this letter reads:

> As the belly of the brute was cut open, out rolled the intestines, and the stench was so dreadful that I could not avert my nausea and had to turn away. But I had the stomach cut out and dragged aside. It was well filled. The contents were instructive and well preserved. The chief contents were young shoots of fir and pine. A quantity of young fir cones, also in a chewed state, were mixed with the mass.
> Windsor Chorlton, *Planet Earth Ice Ages,* p. 54.

Today the closest fir and pine to Benkendorf's mammoth is 1,500 miles away, due south. Since this animal's belly was full of fir and pine shoots, the ecology of Siberia 10,500 years ago was greatly different from today. A fir and pine forest requires a benign temperature range, but the Benkendorf mammoth was found buried in 10,000-year-old permafrost, on the tundra bordering the Arctic Ocean, where the temperature is so low and severe and food so sparse that no mammoth could live there today. This animal was still in a state of preservation. Had it died in a normal fir and pine forest, it would have decomposed quickly, leaving only bones. It *did* die in a fir and pine forest, as its stomach shows, so its preservation can only be accounted for by a sudden and extreme drop in temperature which persisted and eliminated the fir and pine forest by changing it into tundra and permafrost. The temperature change had to be swift for the mammoth would putrefy in four days of its death. Its burial must have been equally swift, or it would have been eaten by scavengers.

Another find is worth recounting, not only because of its scientific importance but also because of the high adventure involved. The Imperial Academy of Science in St. Petersburg (Leningrad), Russia desired to acquire a mammoth carcass for study and display. Reports of a mammoth find along the Beresovka River in the Taiga of fareastern Siberia reached the Academy.[42] An expedition left in May 1900 for the site, arriving in September. The journey required taking the Trans-Siberian Railway across Russia to Yakutska on the Lena River then traveling north 1,500 miles by horse and dogsled to reach the find. A year had passed since the discovery. Humans had taken the tusks; animals had eaten some of the carcass, but it was in overall good shape. They built a tent over the animal and started a fire to thaw it for butchering. The stench became agonizing and the men could only work for brief periods of time. The leader O. F. Herz wrote in his log on October 5, 1900:

> The flesh from under the shoulder, which is fibrous and marbled with fat, is dark red in color and looks as fresh as well-frozen beef or horse meat. It looked so appetizing that we wondered for some time whether we should not taste it, but no one would venture to take it into his mouth, and horseflesh was given the preference. The dogs cleaned up whatever mammoth meat was thrown to them.
> James L. Dyson, *The World of Ice*, p. 148

The animal had partly masticated food between its teeth and 60 pounds of coniferous material in its stomach. This particular animal died from an injury and contained a mass of blood.

Scientists have been aware of frozen animal cadavers in the far northern permafrost for a long time. The first report of a mammoth reached the West in 1692 and many have been found since. The Tungus, especially their dogs, have eaten thousands of them. Their bodies and bones are scattered throughout the permafrost. It is estimated that 10 million mammoths may still exist in the permafrost. Some finds are isolated instances that can date far back, but the vast majority were victims of the 10,500 B.P. catastrophe. James Dyson's observations regarding mammoth finds are poignant:

Many finds were lost to science because they were destroyed before they could be investigated. Many others probably were discovered, but because of remoteness, never were reported. In addition to the carcasses, the tusks and bones of thousand upon thousands of mammoths have been found in the Siberian tundra. In places it must have resembled the North American Great Plains when they were strewn with the bones of bison.

Few if any of the carcasses, except the Adams mammoth, were complete. Most of them consisted of tusks, broken bones, and varying amounts of flesh—often in a state of partial putrefaction—pieces of hide and masses of hair. Many were found because of their odor.

James L. Dyson, *The World of Ice*, p. 145

Unfortunately, very few mammoth finds are reported today. The wretched and poor Siberian natives have every reason not to report them. A reported mammoth is a lost mammoth; on the other hand, the tusks can be taken from an unreported mammoth and sold for $1,000 each. The rate of loss is now greater than ever.

The mammoth relics are so rich that the tusks provide one-third of the world's fossil ivory. The New Siberian Islands, off the mouth of the great Lena River have so many mammoth bones and bones of other grazing animals of the mammoth steppe, that the Russians have mined them with bulldozers for fertilizer. These islands and their surrounding land were above sea level at 10,500 B.P. The fossil record indicates that as time went by during the last Ice Age the number of mammoths steadily increased—right to the end when at 10,500 B.P. they all died and the species became extinct.

What killed the Siberian woolly mammoths and other animals? They were all asphyxiated. The crash of the asteroid made the earth tremble. Then the noise of the impact reached them about sixteen hours later. The Sun and stars had moved and the temperature had dropped because the asteroid's impact had moved the mammoths' Siberian paradise 1,500 miles northward. Then an ink black cloud appeared high in the sky to the west drifting toward the east. It reached them about fifteen days after the impact (measured by the Krakatoa eruption). The cloud has been described. It was a maelstrom of asphyxiating gases, water, magma material, fly ash, and dust. It was totally lethal. The asphyxiating gases which killed the great beasts were followed by mud and rain, tidal waves, floods, and incredible cold.

Only the corpses of very large animals have been found in the Siberian and Alaskan permafrost. The great rains (of many meters deep), tidal waves and floods carried off all the smaller animals into the Arctic Ocean along with many of the larger ones, but left a great number of 6-ton giants scattered along streambeds as the rate of flow dropped, their bodies too heavy to move. Almost all the Siberian mammoth finds have been along rivers. All experts agree that the great mammoths came to a sudden end. That is not disputed; however, there is no agreement as to the cause of the great mass of bones and frozen bodies. To help solve the puzzle as we have, here are more clues, which are accurate observations by authors wondering what happened to the mammoths:

> Practically all mammoth remains have been found in silts and clays deposited by steams or mud flows
> James L. Dyson, *The World of Ice,* p. 165.

We have just described the reason for this.

> Curiously the conditions in which Berkendorf found the mammoth in the Indigirka River may have been similar to those in which it died. The surveyor was surprised to find the carcass was in an upright position, as if the ground on which the animal had stepped, "Thousand of years ago, gave way under the feet of the giant, and he sank as he stood, on all four feet." Since that carcass was lost, the time of its death can only be guessed, but hundreds of other Siberian mammoths have been found in identical positions, suggesting that they perished when a rapid thaw melted the permafrost and turned the tundra into a huge bog.
> Windsor Chorlton, *Planet Earth Ice Ages,* p. 70.

The author is very close to the truth but the facts are different. It was the mud rain the animals stood in. The animals were in absolute blackness. They could not see to move; they were inundated with rain and mud and breathing in asphyxiating gas. There was undoubtedly great heat in the cloud at this time, but the animals were not standing on frozen tundra, that came later. They were standing on the mammoth steppe or in a taiga forest of smaller trees. Most of this terrain would be swept away, any remnants would die and decompose in the forthcoming tundra. Thus, many mammoths died on their feet, supported by the mud of earth and mud from the sky, immobile.

> The condition of the plant remains recovered from mammoth digestive tracts indicates that most animals, at least those examined by scientists, met death late in the summer.
> James L. Dyson, *The World of Ice,* p. 165.

Not quite but very close. By the Gregorian calendar the exact date and time of the asteroid impact was June 5, 8498 B.C. at 8:00 P.M., local time. (Otto Muck, *The Secret of Atlantis*, p. 255) The magnificent behemoths would all die about fifteen days later.

In *Earth's Shifting Crust,* Professor Hapgood addresses the phenomenon of the immense accumulations of bones along the Siberian Arctic. One area is noteworthy, the New Siberian Islands off the mouth of the huge Lena River. Mammoth and large-grazing animal bones have been found there, swept to their current location by a monstrous volume of flowing water.[43] The bones are disarticulated; the animals had been ripped apart before the transport, and then heaped in piles of thousands. They became part of the permafrost, quick-frozen. All the evidence is of a quick and immediate catastrophe, and a cataclysmic change in the weather to temperatures greatly below freezing.

The perfect preservation of thousands of woolly mammoths in the Siberian permafrost for 10,500 years is compelling proof of the suddenness of the temperature change. If the drop in temperature had been a normal atmospheric change, the animals would have spoiled; but they did not and are perfectly intact, which can only come from being quickly frozen, as if in an artificial process. This is shown in the meat of the animals which is well marbled. As the frozen-food industry has proved this can be obtained only when the meat is fast frozen, then kept at a temperature well below freezing. The excellent condition of the tusks also shows evidence of quick freezing. Since the tusks are organic material, they must be frozen and preserved exactly like the meat to be of good quality for carving.

The death of millions of Siberian woolly mammoths was a special case as their demise was caused by the volcanic death cloud with its attendant asphyxiating gases, heat, and violence. Their bodies lie at the very end of a chain of geophysical evidence of the asteroid's impact: the Carolina Bays, the mid-Atlantic crater, the subsidence of the North Atlantic Ridge, the ocean sediment accumulations, the loess belt, the bones and carcasses of Siberia. After the death of the mammoths, millions of megafauna died all over the world within a few centuries. Over half of the megafauna of the earth became extinct, in places far removed from the death cloud, such as Australia. Clearly some other factor was in play that caused the worldwide mass extinction of megafauna. What was it?

First, let us review what species became extinct. More than half of all megafauna Pleistocene mammal species on earth became extinct. And we must remember that this came at the very crest of the golden age of mammals, which had lasted 60 million years up to this time. "The conclusion of the cold period was marked by a toll of death the likes of which had never before afflicted the creatures of the earth." (Windsor Chorlton, *Planet Earth Ice Ages*, p. 65) The repeated glaciations resulted in very large bodies, through Darwinian natural selection. The surviving mammals of today are much smaller in size than the extinct ones. Europe lost 50 percent of its megafauna; North America, 70 percent; North Africa lost many species; South America, 80 percent; Australia, 90 percent. Here are some of the lost species. In North America the Columbian mammoth; a beaver as large as a black bear; the giant ground sloth, several tons weight and 20 feet tall; mastodons; horses, camels, peccaries, dire wolves, llamas, certain deer and pronghorn, saber-toothed cats, giant bison, lions, jaguars, tapirs, plains cat, short-faced bear, glyptodont (a seven-foot armadillo-like animal native to Florida and Texas). Altogether some thirty-five to forty species of large mammals went extinct. In Eurasia the story is the same, with the outstanding loss of the mammoth, the woolly rhino, the monstrous cave bear (thrice as big as any bear extant today), giant deer, and the cave lion. South America lost 80 percent of its large mammals including horses, large armadillos, and huge rodents. In Australia, more than forty species of large mammals (90 percent of the total) became extinct including giant kangaroos, wombats, rhinolike marsupials, and big cats. Overall there is a clear pattern. The large open country animals perished. Of the midsize some survived, some went extinct (all of those which inhabited the open plains), and of the smallest species of mammals (most had some kind of cover) almost all survived. Mammals suffered extinction but so did the predatory birds like eagles, vultures, and condors. These large birds shared the same habitat as the great mammals, the open county.

All authorities agree that, "the crisis did seem to affect the grassland fauna more than the forest animals." (Windsor Chorlton, *Planet Earth Ice Ages*, p.70) And we must remember what North America was like at this time during 10,500 B.P. The ice pressed down to roughly the present Canadian-United States border and south of the Great Lakes. The west was largely dessert; the center a wind swept open plain; the east tundra and boreal forest. Nevertheless, this forbidding environment harbored a great number of animals, concentrated where the best conditions prevailed.

All these magnificent species died very quickly, most within probably five hundred years after the asteroid impact. This was after the ice had begun to melt so weather was not a factor. As to the scavengers such as the saber-toothed cat, the dire wolf, the carrion-eating birds, these could easily have switched from the lost herbivores to the remaining elk, deer, bison, so starvation is not a factor. All of these animal species had been through repeated ice ages and were wonderfully equipped to survive. They were not overhunted by humans. There were almost no human beings in Siberia, yet millions of mammoths perished along with millions of animals of other species. There were very few humans in North America; yet thirty-five to forty species of megafauna became extinct along with the great birds. The numbers alone make the likelihood of overhunting impossible, without even considering the primitiveness of available weapons and the fact that many of these extinct species were of no value to man. The experts admit an unsolved mystery exists. It was stated by Alfred Russell Wallace, codiscoverer of natural selection as the agent of evolution with Charles Darwin in the late 1800s:

> We live in a zoological impoverished world, from which all the hugest, and fiercest, and strangest forms have recently disappeared. It is surely a marvelous fact, and one that has hardly been sufficiently dwelt upon, this sudden dying out of so many large mammals not in one place only but over half the land surface of the globe.
> Windsor Chorlton, *Planet Earth Ice Ages*, p. 55.

And it is well stated by E. C. Pielov:

Could it be that some short-lived catastrophe killed off vast numbers of all large mammals (or all large Herbivores) and that species now extant are those few that managed to build up their numbers again after this catastrophe was over? If so, *what* was the catastrophe? It would have had to have been one that left no evidence of its occurrence and was short lived enough to leave no perceptible gap in the fossil record. All that can now be said is that the cause of the great mammal extinctions is still an unsolved puzzle.

E. C. Pielov, *After the Ice Age*, p. 265.

The cause of the extinction of the great Ice Age megafauna was sterilization caused by hard ultraviolet solar radiation, a potent sterilizer. The radiation occurred because of the asteroid's impact. Resultant volcanic eruptions released freonlike and chlorine gases into the stratosphere that destroyed the ozone layer that protects the earth from ultraviolet radiation, allowing the radiation to reach the surface of the earth in lethal amounts. A secondary cause of the extinction was cosmic particle high-energy hard radiation which greatly increased the rate of harmful mutations in living things. This radiation occurred because the asteroid's impact caused the earth to wobble. This perturbed the earth's magnetic field (that is, the Van Allen radiation belts) which thereafter failed to intercept and hold this type of radiation.

The big animals and big birds died. They were all plains and grassland inhabitants, and they died in a few generations, and the lethal event "left no record of its occurrence and . . . no perceptible gap in the fossil record." The smaller animals and forest denizens had cover during the period of radiation and survived. The death rate depends upon the amount of radiation absorbed by individual animals. Those in the open absorbed the most; those in the forest or underground, the least.

Ultraviolet electromagnetic radiation consists of energy waves traveling at the speed of light in free space. Its source is the Sun. The wavelengths vary from long (harmless radio waves), to medium (harmless visible light), to short (harmful ultraviolet sunlight; X rays and gamma rays—very energetic, readily lethal). A second type of radiation is particulate radiation. Traveling somewhat less than the speed of light, it is composed of highly charged particles that are very energetic and very lethal. Its source is the Sun and deep space. The high-energy forms of radiation are called ionizing or "hard" radiation. This form of radiation causes a chemical reaction in the absorbing body. Lesser penetrating and nonionizing radiation, such as common solar ultraviolet light waves can still cause severe injury such as sunburn, eye injury (snow blindness, burnt retinas), and skin cancer.

Hard ultraviolet radiation is very deadly to animal life. An amazingly small dosage will do great damage, and particular organs are most susceptible to it. These suffer degenerative changes leading to a quick, or delayed death. Bone marrow is the most radiosensitive, then the blood and heart, then the gastrointestinal tract. Male and female reproductive organs are especially susceptible to ultraviolet ionizing radiation and sterility results. Should a pregnant female be irradiated, the fetus would be damaged. This is a time of extraordinary sensitivity to radiation.

Particulate hard radiation produces mutations or sudden variations in inheritable characteristics. Mutations occur in nature with a certain normal rhythm and are in fact the engine that drives plant and animal evolution through the process of natural selection; that is, without mutations there would be no variety within a species to cause it to evolve and change because over time the favorable mutations succeed, reproduce and the unfavorable mutations fail and do not reproduce. The vast majority of mutations are harmful, however. Thus, excessive exposure to particulate hard radiation on an animal species will proportionately increase the mutation rate. It will be detrimental to that species by exactly the amount of increase over the natural mutation rate. Time then is the factor. If the normal rhythm of nature continues, the natural mutation rate is beneficial to life, improving it through natural selection; but if sudden massive radiation occurs "all at once" the result is a disaster of extinction and death. But even if there are survivors, degeneration is the inevitable result because prolonged radiation of a species causes many degenerative factors such as smaller stature, physical weakness, poorer sense of sight, smell and hearing, a reduction in brain volume, a shorter life expectancy, and increased susceptibility to cancer.

A shocking fact of hard radiation injury is that small amounts of radiation exposure will do great damage. This is true of both hard ultraviolet radiation causing sterility and hard particulate radiation causing harmful or deadly mutations. The "linear law" also applies:

Very small doses of radiation given to very large num-

bers of individuals may introduce into the population as many mutant genes as would be introduced through large doses to small numbers of individuals.
Encyclopedia Britannica, Vol. 15, p. 380, 1980.

We might take quick note here of techniques used in pest control. Both sterilization and increased mutation rates are used to eliminate unwanted pests. Insects can be sterilized by irradiation (X rays and gamma rays) or by certain chemicals that destroy or inactivate eggs or sperm. This will also induce fatal genetic changes as one terminal result. Or, a number of male insects may be sterilized and released among the natural population; if the females breed infrequently and not promiscuously, there will be a reduction in fertile eggs laid and a resulting population reduction. If the number of sterile matings exceed that of fertile matings, over some generations, the natural population will become extinct. All in all, a very close parallel to the cause of the megafauna extinction of 10,500 B.P. at the end of the Ice Age.

The earth is protected from radiation from the Sun and cosmos by two extraterrestrial phenomena: the ozone layer and the Van Allen radiation belts. The ozone layer protects the earth from hard ultraviolet (sterilizing) radiation; the ozone layer exists between 12 to 30 miles (20km and 50km) above the earth's surface. It has the vital property of absorbing solar ultraviolet radiation, but it is extremely sensitive to air density, water vapor, and certain gases which can destroy it. There really is very little of it. If it were compressed to sea level, it would be a layer only a half-inch thick. Just how important is it? The *Encyclopedia Britannica* 1980 Macro, Vol. 6 states at page 711:

> This zone (that is., ozone) is highly important for life on earth because it absorbs most of the ultraviolet radiation from the Sun; if this penetrated to the earth's surface it would act as a potent sterilizer, fatal to most forms of life. It also helps to maintain a more uniform surface temperature by reducing the loss of heat by radiation to space—the so-called greenhouse effect.

Earth's second defense from radiation are the two Van Allen radiation belts that encircle the earth between 500 to 3,000 miles and between 6,000 to 40,000 miles. The belts are products of the earth's magnetic field and serve to trap high-energy protons and electrons that are the mutation causing particulate radiation, which originate from the Sun and cosmic sources. The belts were first discovered by James Alfred Van Allen in 1958 during the course of early rocket upper atmosphere exploration. The existence of this radiation trap is essential to life to prevent harmful and deadly mutations.

But the asteroid's impact and aftermath caused huge damage to these two protective phenomena and severely damaged life on earth. The ozone layer was destroyed by the continent-sized cloud caused by the North Atlantic volcanic eruption. Its very height exceeded the ozonosphere. Its gaseous content contained Freon type gas (chlorofluorocarbons) and especially chlorine. Both gases will destroy the fragile and rarefied ozone layer. Earth's second vitally important protective shield from deadly radiation from the Sun and space, the Van Allen radiation belts, was destroyed by quite another effect of the asteroid's impact, the increased wobble of the earth's axis. The earth's pole of axial rotation (the true North Pole) and the electromagnetic North Pole are always very close together, although they change over the eons. The earth's axis of rotation moved 2° toward the point of the asteroid impact. This increased the "wobble" of the earth, which gradually dissipated according to known gyroscopic physics. The wobble perturbed the earth's magnetic field, along with the Van Allen radiation belts, which then allowed high-energy hard particulate radiation to reach the surface of the earth. The first five hundred years after the impact were the worst. Thereafter, the earth's magnetic field stabilized and the Van Allen belts resumed their protective function.

Thus, many species of great animals died, the victims of hard radiation. These genera died quickly, extinct in a few hundred years after millions of years on earth, primarily due to sterilization—the quickest and surest route to mass extinction. But again note that it was the large animal that became extinct. All plains and open country animals, and the smaller and forest-dwelling animals survived, because they had cover from the radiation while the large open country animals did not.

Even during the worst of the radiation event, some cover would have helped given species to survive. Hard, ultraviolet radiation has low-penetrating power, and the body can be shielded by forest cover (or in the case of Homo sapiens, clothes), but the great animals of the Mammoth Steppe, the plains, and open country had no cover. Like all living things they relished the sunlight, and it killed them. Is this eerily familiar? What about the dinosaurs that so mysteriously perished at the Cretaceous-Tertiary boundary 65 million years ago? Some scientists suspect an asteroid impact but provide absolutely no evidence of what happens after that.[44] Yes, exactly the same thing happened, and the same result was obtained. The large open country dinosaurs became extinct, and the small protected mammals survived, one becoming Homo sapiens, the only animal capable of worrying about what happened, albeit 65 million years and another asteroid later. And what did happen to man? How was he affected by the catastrophic asteroid impact of 10,500 years ago and the subsequent hard radiation? Let us reserve that discussion for "Part V: Man Recovers."

Part V: Man Recovers

CHAPTER 20: CIVILIZATIONS SUDDENLY APPEAR

After the asteroid impact, there is a long silence on the world stage. Ice and permafrost covers one-third of the earth, deserts one-third, and now the remaining one-third—man's habitat—has been hit with horrible devastation. Most of the earth's Northern Hemisphere and much of the northern part of the Southern Hemisphere have been wiped out. The track of the cataclysm in the form of the continent-sized death cloud is evident: It is the loess belt that extends from west to east at a latitude just above the Mediterranean Sea. The cloud extended on each side of this belt and because of the prevailing winds eventually encircled the earth and killed everything in its path. Closer to the equator, the trade winds carried the death cloud from east to west, devastating Central America and northern South America. The release of an enormous amount of carbon dioxide from the oceans into the atmosphere caused global warming and the great North American ice sheets began a swift retreat. They melted to their present locations in the geologically impossible brief span of 4,000 years. The melting would have occurred at a faster rate, compounding the catastrophe had it not been for residual, minute dust particles that remained in the atmosphere for up to 2,000 years and reflected the sun's heat back into space. As the clouds drifted north and south because of the Coriolis effect, unfiltered radiation hit the earth, causing the extinction of approximately 70 percent of the large fauna due to sterilization and harmful mutations.

An observer of the world scene would assume that mankind had been wiped out. The worst damage occurred in the very area where humans lived. In fact a very noticeable gap in history occurs between 10,500 and 5000 B.P. (known as the Mesolithic or Middle Stone Age). There is an eerie silence. Anthropologists and archaeologists detect no movement by man and no new significant archeological finds. It is as though contact with the past has been severed. Thor Heyerdahl says in *The Tigris Expedition*:

> As distinct from the Ra experiments, we had sailed in *Tigris* to trace the beginning of history according to Sumerian writings. This had brought us to Dilmun, where the Sumerians said their forefathers had settled after the world catastrophe when most of mankind drowned. When listening to ancient man's opinion about our beginnings, we can nowhere get past the stories of a flood. Long before Christianity reached Hellas, the Greeks had three different versions of this disastrous flood: they had their own original deluge in which it was their own supreme god Zeus who had punished mankind; then, already in pre-Christian times, they received a Hebrew variant from the Hellenistic Jews; and independent of both of these they had received the Egyptian version following their intimate contact with the Nile Country. If we care for the opinion of the ancient people whose cultural origin we seek, we have to bear with their flood stories, which obstruct everything beyond.
> (Thor Heyerdahl, *The Tigris Expedition*, p. 328)

But around 5000 B.P. things change. Human presence in the Mideast and middle America is again detected and suddenly civilizations appear. These are full blown right from the start to the bewilderment of anthropologists. In fact, this recovery by man who is moving back into the devastated areas is mistakenly called "The Birth of Civilization in the Mid East." It should be called "The Rebirth of Civilization in the Mid East."[45]

The first people to move back were the Sumerians around 3500 B.C. Their place of origin is unknown, but wherever it was, their ancestors had escaped the asteroid impact catastrophe.[46] They arrived at the lower Tigris-Euphrates by boat (reed ships) and were from the beginning accomplished traders and seafarers; in all ways, they were incredibly advanced—the first light in an otherwise culturally dark world. They settled the lower Tigris-Euphrates Valley near the Persian Gulf in thirteen city-states. Because this civilization is the first to appear after the catastrophe, it would retain strong vestiges of the First Civilization. From the very first, Sumerian society was absolutely complete. They had a fluent language that expressed poetry and tax bills and a cuneiform (wedge-shaped) form of writing that expressed their spoken language (unlike Chinese characters). The lucky recovery of about one thousand clay tablets at Uruk has provided great insight into Sumerian life. They include inventory of cattle, sheep, goats and their exchange, instructions regarding irrigation, medicine, metalworking, legal documents, school texts, tax bills, songs; letters—anything and everything. The basic economy of the city-states was agriculture. Crops were wheat, barley, vegetables, dates; domestic animals were cattle, sheep, goats, and pigs. Fishing was important. Society included nobles, priests, merchants, tradesmen, scribes, and slaves. Trade and commerce was particularly active. Ships plied the rivers with all sorts of cargo; sailing ships crossed the ocean to India. Each city had a great brick ziggurat and other public works. Their religion was polytheistic, and they practiced human sacrifice. The end finally came as a result of war in the form of constant invasions by the Semitic peoples of the West. Upon the demise of the Sumerian civilization, these Semitic conquerors formed the states of Assyria in the north and Babylon in the south. The familiar march of history begins. But everything starts with Sumer.

The second people to move back were the Egyptians about 3000 B.C., a few centuries after Sumer's beginning. Again, their provenance is unknown. This civilization arises also spontaneously, in full flower, displacing the mud huts of a few earlier dwellers with great monumental structures. Their knowledge of astronomy displayed a scientific proficiency that required thousands of years to develop. Just as in the Tigris-Euphrates basin there was no local buildup from the crude dwellings of the few prior inhabitants to the heights of Egyptian civilization; the invaders brought the civilization with them.

Like Sumer, the arrival of civilization was abrupt; a total change came to the environs of the Nile overnight. Agriculture, domestic animals, irrigation began providing the requisite foundation for a large population. Many people were able to accumulate wealth manifested in elaborate burial rituals and public works. The pyramids, marvels for all time, are a mixture of incredible construction ability and science of the highest degree. The specifics of pyramid construction are still unknown. The Arabs have always held that the pyramids, especially the largest, that of Cheops (Khufu) built 2650 B.C., were built not only as tombs but also as repositories of knowledge and as geographic landmarks for surveying and navigation. Modern scholarship has borne this out. In all, some eighty pyramids were built in Egypt during the Pyramid Age from 2686 to 1777 B.C., starting with the stepped pyramid of Zoser (the Pharaoh) and ending in a shabby fashion with deterioration in size and quality.[47] Egyptian society as a whole started an inexorable downhill slide. By 1300 B.C., all the promise of this great civilization was gone.

A third spontaneous mideastern civilization appeared in the Indus Valley, India. It suddenly appears at 2500 B.C. as a full-fledged civilization and lasted one thousand years, then vanished for unknown reasons. Agriculture supplied the economic base, with crops of wheat, barley, dates, melons, peas, mustard, cotton, and domestic animals as cattle, buffalo, pigs, chickens, sheep, elephants, camels, asses, dogs, and cats. The structure of the cities in the Indus Valley shows planning and government control. The cities are similar in layout, with amenities such as public water, flowing sewers and organized housing in rows of two-room units. The public works were mostly of a practical nature such as granaries, defense works and administrative buildings. This civilization is not as advanced as Mesopotamia's or Egypt's.

These three civilizations traded extensively with one another and with other peoples, such as the island of Bahrain. All three appeared at about the same time and all followed a similar course: brilliant in the beginning and then falling off, degenerate and retrogressive. All three appeared suddenly "spontaneously" and "came from somewhere else." All three bore with them elements of civilization which they instantly displayed without any evidence of historical buildup such as domesticated animals and crops, crafts, architectural techniques, maritime ability, astronomy, and science.

Egypt should be singled out for its scientific achievements. Its civilization was established at 3000 B.C., and the Great Pyramid of Cheops was built at 2650 B.C. incorporating sophisticated scientific data, a feat far too great for a people "civilized" only 350 years. This is only one example of a common point; all three civilizations produced works far beyond their ability when measured by the short time span of their existence. Their original expertise came from the First Civilization but its heritage was gradually lost for various reasons. Some reasons are known such as war, societal breakdown, and some are suspected like lack of attention to scientific matters, rise in influence of an irrational religion or oppression of the populace; however, most remain unknown. Thus, the rebirth of civilization in the Mideast failed.

A fourth civilization, the Olmec, spontaneously appeared an ocean away in Mesoamerica. The Olmec appeared suddenly, spontaneously, in full flower with all the accoutrements of a long-established civilization. This civilization and its successors, the Maya, Aztec, and Inca are of great interest because they were still intact in 1492; and they were seen by European man, who promptly destroyed them to such a horrific degree it has been said we know more about the civilizations of the Mideast than we do of Mesoamerica. The Olmecs first appear about 1400 B.C. on the Caribbean coast of Central America just north of the Yucatán Peninsula. They appear suddenly displacing some primitive inhabitants; they came from somewhere else and possessed a fully formed civilization which anthropologists believe later spread over the rest of Mesoamerica. The Olmec civilization was a paramount cause of the rise of the later Teotihuacán civilization (Valley of Mexico, later conquered by the Aztecs then by Cortés), the Incan civilization of Peru and the Mayan. Olmec culture continued in the Mesoamerican heartland but disappeared as an entity between 900–400 B.C. from unknown causes. Thus, the Olmec culture failed, as did the first Mideast civilizations; however, in a different way, as its cultural vibrancy was taken up quite directly by the Teotihuacán civilization, by the Mayas and, less directly, by the Incas.

The Olmecs created the first post 10,500 B.P. true cities in the New World at San Lorenzo and LaVenta. Step pyramids promptly appear, along with buildings, ball courts, monuments, stele (inscribed stone), stepped platforms, in short, complete urban architecture exactly like the earliest mideastern architecture. The economic basis for life was agriculture called "swidden" or "slash and burn" which is suited to heavy tropical vegetation by employing many small plots of land. It rains in the summer in Mesoamerica, so all the vegetation on a plot is cut in the winter and burned thus clearing the land and providing ash as fertilizer. Crops are sown in winter and harvested in summer (maize, beans, squash). Swidden is a wasteful system. After two years the land must lie fallow to recover or production will fall to an impractical level. The fallow time required is lengthy (up to twenty years!) and 70 to 90 percent of the land may be fallow at one time. Hunting, fishing, and gathering wild plants supplemented the diet. Small gardens produced vegetables, fruit trees, and poultry (turkey, duck, pigeon). The Olmecs were scientific and probably produced the Mayan calendar, notable for its great antiquity and accuracy. The Olmecs had writing of the hieroglyphic sort, a system of mathematics using bars and dots, and were astronomers (but with exquisitely little time to perfect their magnificent calendar if we assume their civilization started at 1400 B.C.). Strangely, the place picked by the Olmecs for their heartland was woefully unsuited for the purpose. The soil was poor, much of the land was swampy, the forest was almost a jungle. It was subject to fires, storms, floods, weeds, and tropical plant diseases. It had one thing going for it: it was exactly at the end of the north edge of the Canary Current. It had received one-fourth of the immigrants from North Africa before 10,500 B.P. (using 1492 demographics) and as the Olmec civilization appeared well after the mideastern civilizations, it had the benefit of some contact with those civilizations, as well as China and Black Africa.

Thus, the rebirth of civilization in the New World follows the same pattern as the three in the Old World. In an area barely inhabited by primitive people there suddenly appears a new civilization in full force built by people who came from somewhere else, and it slowly regresses and fails. The matter of the sudden or spontaneous creation of these four reemerging civilizations requires some thought. A well-taken dogma of anthropology is that it takes a long time, thousands of years, to create a civilization from the primitive beginnings of hunter-gatherers. Yet, for some inexplicable reason, the most conservative and reactionary anthropologists blithely pass over just how this sudden and spontaneous development of these four civilizations was made possible. Of course the answer is obvious, heritage of knowledge from the First Civilization. However, these worthies will not admit this, as they do not believe a prior civilization existed. This leaves them having to accept phenomena, a miracle, as a fact, for which they have no explanation.

Reemerging civilizations are not the only measure of man's recovery. There are other matters that should be noted. The world's weather had vastly changed. The great ice sheets had retreated to their present positions by 6500 B.P., exposing vast amounts of land to human habitation. But no new civilization spontaneously appears here. The four that did reappear, did so in exactly the same places where there had been civilizations before 10,500 B.P. The Sahara has not recovered because although ice-age aridity is gone new weather factors are in play. The continuous high pressure in the 30° latitudes over Asia, feeds dry air to the east-west trade winds and gives this great landmass no moisture. The

Amazon Basin is quite different from before 10,500 B.P. The world's warmer ambient air temperature and the Atlantic's warmer water temperature caused more rainfall in this area and produced a huge tropical forest, making it much less desirable for human habitation. Primitive people still inhabit it but civilized people would prefer to live elsewhere. The slow foresting of the Amazon Basin caused man to move into all parts of South America. In Central America the post-10,500 B.P. pressure to expand the area of human habitation came from overpopulation. Monumental structures are a sure measure of population. After the disappearance of the Olmec and the emergence of the Mayan and Teotihuacán civilizations hundreds of cities, pyramid complexes, and irrigated areas appear, all bespeaking a heavy population load. A Central American migration into North America took place. The base area was east of the Mississippi River and the migration moved north through the woodlands east of the Mississippi which produced an amazing abundance of food. Early Spanish explorers of the southeastern part of the United States (for example, Hernando de Soto from 1538 to 1542) found a highly developed agricultural economy of Central American provenance. It was so quickly wiped out by European introduced disease that most American history texts barely mention it, if at all. Organized agricultural communities existed in pre-Columbian times well up into the Great Lakes area. Over the rest of the North American continent a sparse population of Indians lived by hunter gathering and followed the retreating ice northward.

Europe, always a backwater, had small, tribal populations at the time of the reemergence of the two mideastern civilizations. Settlements and fortifications begin to appear at 4000 B.P. Thereafter, agriculture became widespread. There is evidence of rapidly spreading small-scale warfare over desirable territory. Europe progressed slowly until it is seen in vivid relief at the time of the Roman conquest of Gaul and Britain. In 1994, a singular event gave European anthropology a great boon. This was the discovery of a 5,300-year-old body of a man in the Alps. This find is carefully detailed in *The Man In The Ice* by Konrad Spindler, who led the scientific team investigating the find. The Iceman lived when the Great Pyramid was built. He lived in a mountain valley, and was probably a shepherd who went up into the Alps (now the Italian Tyrol) and dressed accordingly. He wore a fine fur hat, a magnificent fur cape that would have looked good on Park Avenue when new, a loincloth, fur leggings, and fur boots lined with grass. He carried a backpack with an external wooden frame and leather bag (not invented by modern man until the 1930s), a bow and arrows and a wood ax with a copper blade. Seventeen pieces of wood, each a different species, were used in his equipment, each one the best selection for the job. The Iceman was sophisticated and modern in his own way. Some European peasants dressed like this until the 1960s. He was very intelligent, confined only by the technological limits of his time and place, and not by his intellectual capacity. The Iceman gives us several good lessons: never underestimate the ability of ancient man; never assume that the only things of historical importance come from the glittering ancient monumental works, and by comparison, the rest of the world is primitive and far less important; never generalize from the 'primitive' items uncovered in an archaeological dig that these items reflect the overall status of man's accomplishments. From the Iceman how would we guess the Pyramids which were under construction at the time of the Iceman's death?

CHAPTER 21: CULTURAL EVIDENCE OF THE FIRST CIVILIZATION

In "Part III: The First Civilization" the physical remnants of that civilization were discussed. This point of view gave us a tantalizing look at this civilization's scope and geographical extent. "Part IV: The Asteroid" details the cause of its destruction. "Part V: Chapter 20: Civilizations Suddenly Appear" briefly summarizes the reemergence of four disparate civilizations. Now this question is posed: What cultural facets of these four civilizations come from the First Civilization? A subject will be selected (ships, legends, agriculture, etc.) and will be examined accordingly to three criteria:

1. Natural progress
2. Contact
3. Heritage
   a. Of imaginative subject matter
   b. Not enough time to develop this skill
   c. Unique and very old, pre-10,500 B.P.

Natural progress in the chronological development of a civilization is to be expected and does not help us in our search for cultural remnants of the First Civilization. Natural progress includes matters of everyday life such as clothing, stone and copper/bronze tools, and common shelters. Contact refers to visits and trade between the civilizations whereby one civilization could acquire goods and knowledge from the other (for example, Egypt from Mesopotamia; the New World from the Old World). Heritage refers to a direct legacy from the First Civilization. It applies only when this is the only explanation for the given phenomenon; subcategories a, b, and c are three reasons why heritage applies.

The very earliest ships and seafaring are a heritage from the First Civilization. The fact that the First Civilization possessed excellent watercraft (ships and rafts) is shown by Professor Hapgood's maps of the American and African coastlines, the North Atlantic and Antarctica, all done before 10,500 B.P. Further proof is the conveyance of thousands of people from North Africa to the New World before 10,500 B.P. Since ship design remains unchanged for thousands of years a study of the earliest ships and rafts known to archaeology (5000 B.P. to present) is a look at the heritage from the First Civilization. The ship unearthed by the Great Pyramid in the 1950s is over 4,500 years old. It dates from the earliest part of Egyptian civilization, but it is beautiful and modern. It is made of cedar, 141 feet long, displaces 40 tons and is an oceangoing sailing ship and is better designed than the Viking's long ships or Columbus' caravels. Only a long history of sailing on the open sea could account for such a ship. But with the date of 5000 B.P. taken as the beginning of Egyptian civilization and looking backward in time, we enter "The Gap" in history (the Mesolithic age). There are only primitive people and no civilization to account for the scientific effort that produced this ship until we enter the time period of the First Civilization which ended at 10,500 B.P. The skill required to produce this ship is a heritage from the First Civilization. This conclusion is established because the reemerging Egyptian civilization did not have enough time to develop the skills necessary to produce this ship. Its design and method of construction is a heritage from the First Civilization.

Reed boats have endured from the very beginning of the Old World reemerging civilizations to the present time. Sumerian scribes recorded their belief that shipbuilding and navigation had been learned from ancestors (or gods) long departed. Their frescoes show reed boats, (and the Sumerians arrived at Mesopotamia by boat), as does Egyptian art. Thus, the Sumerian and Egyptian civilizations first appear fully proficient in the art of shipbuilding (wood and reed), sailing, and to a limited extent navigation. Only heritage can explain this instant sophistication with no time for a progressive buildup.

Reed boats were available to all. The only tools required to build one are a knife (stone works well) and rope. With minimum skill a reed boat is easy to construct, and it is quite seaworthy enough to sail the Atlantic, facts proved by Heyerdahl. And those ancient ships could be large, quite capable of transporting thousands of people across the Atlantic Ocean. Some Egyptian ships were 250 feet long. Heyerdahl in the late 1970s saw huge reed rafts moored along the Euphrates River and measured one at 112 feet long, 16.5 feet wide, 10 feet deep. Such a raft could carry 40 tons of cargo but Heyerdahl reports ancient records from Uruk that describe merchant vessels capable of carrying 100 tons.[48] An Indus Valley port, Lothal was constructed in 4300 B.P. for oceangoing trade (docks, warehouses and all) and was designed for ships 59 to 65 feet long, 13 to 20 feet wide which must have been a standard size. Unfortunately, Lixus, the Moroccan starting point on a voyage to the New World has not been excavated adequately to describe its port facilities.

In the New World reed boats are still used on Lake Titicaca for fishing; Heyerdahl employed four Indians from that area to construct *Ra II* in Africa. Reed boats were used throughout Central America and Baja California until very recently (early 1900s) and in the Pacific Ocean as far as Easter Island. In Africa the boats were made of papyrus, in the Americas and Easter Island from the totora reed; both plants grow in freshwater and thus require transplanting by man, ocean drift will not do. Man carried the transplanted reeds to the volcanic crater of Easter Island and to Lake Titicaca at 12,000 feet. The range of reed boats, concomitant papyrus and totora reeds extends westward through Mesopotamia, Egypt, various Mediterranean islands, the Atlantic Coast of Morocco, Mexico, and Peru. This is a road map of the First Civilization. Reed boats appear fully developed at the earliest stage of the four reemerging civilizations on both sides of the Atlantic. Was it natural progress, contact, or heritage? Their earliest possible appearance in the Mideast in fully developed form rules out natural progress; there was no developmental phase. There was no contact with an older, superior civilization skilled in shipbuilding and seafaring because no such civilization existed. Heritage supplies the only answer for all three reasons. It took imagination or "a mind's eye" to conceive of and build a reed boat with sails suitable for the high seas; it took skill to build a reed ship and to sail it. They appear at the dawn of the reemerging civilizations, and there was no time to develop these skills. Reed boats are unique and very old. Reed ships were a product of the First Civilization and used long before 10,500 B.P.

Rafts were the superb watercraft of the New World which was blessed with big trees, especially balsa trees of northern South America. Rafts of enormous size could be constructed. Equipped with sail and centerboards, they were capable of any voyage a conventionally designed ship could do and carried a lot more. These rafts were especially concentrated off Peru's Pacific Coast and used for fishing and trade. In fact they had plied vast reaches of the Pacific Ocean as the Incas divulged to the Spaniards. (All of this is described in Heyerdahl's *Early Man and the Ocean*.) On his mission of treachery and conquest of Peru, Pizarro encountered a flotilla of Inca rafts. Thereafter, the Spaniards commandeered them for their own purposes as they were capable of heavy cargo, could approach shore and unload. A conventional ship could not. Just before the Spanish conquest of Peru, Inca Tupac voyaged in the South Seas for one year with 20,000 men on hundreds of balsa rafts. Such rafts were continuously in use until about 1900 when they finally were replaced by European-type boats. The keys to their longevity were simplicity of construction, seaworthiness of the balsa logs, tracking ability through sail, centerboards, a steering oar, and the ability to land in surf. In his fabulous adventure narrated in the book *Kon-Tiki*, Heyerdahl describes his 4,300-mile, 101-day float from Peru to Tahiti's Raroia reef, forever ending doubts about such a watercraft's ability to sail the open sea.

We must note some of the voyages of the mariners of ancient times because they measure the ability of their predecessors in the First Civilization to do the same thing or better and to populate the New World. But even before starting, a vital point must be made: trade voyages were kept in ironclad secrecy. Death was the lot of a sailor who talked about going to Britain for tin, or to the American Great Lakes for copper, or to South America and South Africa for various products. There is an old tale of a Phoenician ship that cleared Gibraltar and then turned north for Britain for a cargo of tin; it could not shake a following Roman ship. The Phoenician captain took his ship near the Spanish shore and sank it. The men swam ashore and walked across Spain to return home. Secrecy resulted in a total lack of records of many far-flung voyages. This has made academicians apoplectic when Phoenician inscriptions, Egyptian motifs, and Roman coins appear where they do not belong, in the New World.

Herodotus recounts a Phoenician expedition that circumnavigated Africa about 600 B.C., sailing from east to west (that is, clockwise). Upon return, the voyagers reported that when turning Africa the sun rose in the north instead of the south. This was taken as a lie at the time, and Herodotus was ostracized for telling the story. Two thousand years later, the Portuguese proved Herodotus and the Phoenician sailors to be correct, verifying that the voyage had actually occurred. In 500 B.C., Himlico of Carthage sailed north along the European coast. He reached the North Sea and described the whaling grounds of the Bay of Biscay. Hanno of Carthage mounted a great expedition in 475 to 480 B.C. It consisted of sixty ships of fifty oars each, containing 30,000 men and women to be colonizers along the North African Atlantic coast, which Carthage had already colonized for 800 years and had established 300 colonies. The interesting thought is the return trip. Hanno was to go south beyond the "bulge of Africa." Upon return, he would catch the adverse Canary Current as he fought the east to west trade wind. A storm could easily head the ships toward the Americas. Quite a few historians believe something like this did happen. It is noteworthy to observe why the Carthaginians sought to colonize. Carthage was located on the Mediterranean Sea in western North Africa. While the Sahara was becoming ever dryer, Carthage's population was growing. It was the biggest city in the world at this time of over one million people. They needed new living space—just like the First Civilization eight thousand years before. In conclusion: The very earliest ships and seafaring represent heritage from the First Civilization.

The pyramids of the four reemerging civilizations practically scream "heritage." There was no natural progression as pyramids were the first significant structures built by the suddenly arrived civilizations. There was trade contact between the Sumerians, Indus Valley, and Egyptians, but it had nothing to do with pyramids. These were monumental structures of little practical value, but held in great cultural esteem and reflected favorably on the rulers and priests, magnifying their importance. These structures, obviously reconstituted a prior design and plan much like Christian churches and Islamic mosques repeat themselves. This is clearly seen when—astonishingly—step pyramids just like those found in Sumeria are found in the New World (Olmec 1200 to 300 B.C.), long after they have fallen into disuse in the Old World. "The Great Pyramid Age" in Egypt was from 2682 to 2181 B.C. but inferior pyramids were built until 1777 B.C. Since the pre-Columbian contact with the Old World was sporadic, only for trade, and the Old World had lost its interest in pyramids—there was no reason for the Olmecs, the Maya, Aztecs, or Inca to duplicate a discontinued item. Thus contact was not the reason for the building of the Mexican pyramids so this can only be explained by heritage from the First Civilization and all three of our basic reasons apply: a) the pyramids are very much products of the imagination, not likely to be developed by coincidence; b) there was not enough time to develop the skill required in their construction (building technique, astronomical features such as astronomical alignment, observatories, integration with religion) as they appeared immediately; and c) the design is unique and very old, and it first appears as a finished design, hence it crosses "the gap" of the moribund Mesolithic (10,500 to 5000 B.P.) to the First Civilization.

The first pyramids appear in Sumeria (3000 B.C.) with the sudden and spontaneous arrival of this civilization. They are called ziggurats, a description of their step-pyramid shape. They were made of mud brick. Mesopotamia had no stone for their construction, unlike Egypt, and they are poorly preserved. Their walls and ascending staircases make them of identical class with the first pyramid of Egypt (circa Zoser 2686 B.C.) and of the Olmec in Central America (1200 to 300 B.C.). The first pyramid in Egypt is the Zoser step pyramid built on high ground near Memphis, Egypt (several hundred miles South of Giza), with the famed and later deified Imhotep as architect. It was part of a complex of buildings surrounded by a wall and was used as a tomb by the Pharaoh Zoser and his family. Very shortly the Great Pyramid is built (circa 2650 B.C.) at Giza during the reign of Pharaoh Cheops; it is a true pyramid, not a step pyramid. A wonder of the world for all time; its base covers 13.1 acres, is 756 feet on a side, rises to a height of 481 feet with its four sides having an angle of 51°52'. Its sides are oriented to true north, south, east, and west. It contains 2,300,000 blocks of stone with an average weight of 3 tons. Originally it had a casing of beautiful white limestone (now gone to make mosques and buildings in Cairo) and a "capstone" thought to have represented an eye, a symbol of Ra the Sun God, but the top 31 feet of the Great Pyramid are now missing. The 50-ton granite roof slabs of the King's Chamber were loaded on barges (reed perhaps?) at Aswan and floated 500 miles on the Nile River to Giza when the river was high and fast. Exactly how a block was unloaded, taken across land and raised into place is unknown but modern engineers guess that sledges and ramps were used. After this fabulous achievement, pyramid building fell into sudden decline and all subsequent specimens were remarkably inferior. The last of eighty pyramids built was the Pyramid of Khender in 1777 B.C. at Saqqar (30 miles south of Giza).[49]

The Indus Valley did not produce pyramids; it was a tightly organized society with a strong central authority evidenced by the large, orderly cities, laid out on grid systems. But there are no pyramids, palaces, great tombs, and other nonutilitarian structures. The explanation is lacking. Perhaps this is a clue that the Indus Valley was out of the range of the First Civilization, or its form of government (social organization) was quite different from deified monarchs. Unfortunately, the archaeological record is quite inadequate.

The Central American pyramids observed by the conquistadors greatly resemble the step pyramids of Sumer and Egypt. They have the same step design and are part of a complex oriented to the cardinal points of the compass (but not exactly!). Central America's greatest example is found in the ruins of Teotihuacán, near Mexico City. It was a ruin when overtaken by the Aztecs A.D. 1100 to A.D. 1200; it is three pyramids connected by the Street of the Dead (Aztec name) aligned 15°30' east of true north. The three pyramids uncannily imitate the three large pyramids at Giza. The Central Americans go the Egyptians one better. At Cholula they built a four-tier step pyramid that is the largest building in the world. It is 200 feet high and its sides at the base are 1,500 feet long, twice the length of the sides of the Great Pyramid at Giza. As with many pyramids in Egypt and Central America, it was rebuilt or expanded several times—a new larger pyramid was built over the old. It is estimated to be two thousand years old and was in use until A.D. 1200, built by a succession of different cultures. A true Olmec pyramid at LaVenta was built in the form of a fluted cone 100 feet tall and 200 feet in diameter. Oddly, the site axis points at 8° west of true north.

Contact with the Old World cannot explain the resemblances of Teotihuacán and the other Mexican pyramids to Sumer and Egypt. A few boatloads of sailors would not know where to begin such a project. Only heritage from the First Civilization can account for such magnificent and identical pyramids as constructed by three of the four reemerging civilizations. And once again, the loss of contact between the Old World and the New World from 10,500 B.P. to A.D. 1492 proves heritage is the answer as the New World's efforts are entirely independent of the Old World's efforts, yet there is near exact duplication.

For a long time scholars have believed that originally (let us use this word to mean during the Ice Age up to 10,500 B.P.) Homo sapiens had only one language, which was worldwide. The subject is intangible and very far-reaching with conclusive proof impossible, but it is fair to say that this is the near unanimous opinion of philologists who have addressed the issue. There is far too much resemblance between geographically separate languages to assign this fact to coincidence. In *The Masks of God: Primitive Mythology,* Joseph Campbell states:

> As early as 1767 a French Jesuit in India, Father Coeurdoux, had observed that Sanskrit and Latin were remarkably alike. Sir William Jones (1746 to 1794)—The west's first considerable Sanskritist, judge of the supreme court of judicature at Calcutta, and founder of the Bengal Asiatic Society— was the next to observe the relationship, and from a comparative study of the grammatical structures of Latin, Greek and Sanskrit concluded that all three had "sprung" as he phrased it "from some common source, which perhaps no longer exists." Franz Bopp (1791 to 1867) published in 1816 a comparative study of the Sanskrit, Greek, Latin, Persian, and Germanic systems of conjugation. And finally, by the middle of the century it was perfectly clear that a prodigious distribution of closely related tongues could be identified over the greater part of the civilized world; a single, broadly scattered family of languages that must have sprung from a single source, and which includes, besides Sanskrit and Pali (the language of the Buddhist scriptures), most of the tongues of northern India as well as Singhalese (the language of Ceylon), Persian, Armenian, Albanian, and Bulgarian; Polish, Russian, and the other Slavic tongues; Greek, Latin and all the languages of Europe except Estonian, Finnish, Lapp, Magyar, and Basque. Thus a continuum from Ireland to India had been revealed. And not only the languages, but also the civilizations and religions, mythologies, literary forms, and modes of thought of the peoples involved could be readily compared: for example, the Vedic pantheon of ancient India, the Eddic of medieval Iceland, and the Olympian of the Greeks. No wonder the leading scholars and philosophers of the century were impressed!
> (Joseph Campbell, *The Masks of God: Primitive Mythology,* p. 9)

Special mention should be made of the Basque language. Some scholars call it unique and perhaps the closest of all the languages to the Ice Age original.

Just as scholars find the root of modern languages to be universal, similarly they find a common universal root for the world's mythologies.

Campbell finds "...the worldwide diffusion of the major themes of classical as well as biblical mythology and religious lore." (p. 13) He further states: "From this momentous decade of the (eighteen) sixties onward, the universality of the basic themes and motifs of mythology was generally conceded." (p. 14) Campbell cites death-and-resurrection, the virgin birth and spontaneous creation as examples of common mythological themes. A masterpiece of scholarship that inventories many of the myths of the world exists in *The Golden Bough* by Sir James George Frazer (1890). This text is a large work and hard reading, but no one can doubt the universality of mythology after reading it. A late entry into the field is *Hamlet's Mill* by de Santillana and von Dechend. The major theme of the book is that many an unprepossessing myth is actually a carrier of basic astronomical information. Out of hundreds of myths one is emphasized "The Fall of Phaëthon" as an obvious astronomical analogy—and it is (that is, the story of the chariot going too close to the Sun, catching fire, dropping and burning the earth). The authors did not have the benefit of Otto Muck's book and do not recognize the myth as a story of an asteroid fall, but they are correct. It absolutely is a classic astronomical myth, and it is a part of the worldwide family of myths that describe the fall of the asteroid in 10,500 B.P. (the fall of the "Feathered Serpent" in Central America; the "sun and stars move" in other geographical areas). Thus, the First Civilization has imparted knowledge to us about itself, if we only know how to look for it. We look at the reemerging civilizations and realize that they did have and used much knowledge from the First Civilization in establishing their own. At first material objects catch our eye as ships and pyramids and everyday commonalities, but then we see evidence of it in intangible items such as religion, language, and mythology which are universal and have a common origin, the First Civilization.

Of paramount concern in our investigation of culture derived from the First Civilization is the comparison of the New World Civilization to the Old World Civilizations, because of the loss of communication between the two from 10,500 B.P to 1492. The commonalities between the New World and the Old World are strong proof that both derived much of their culture from the First Civilization by heritage. This is particularly true the more "imaginative" the culture item is (for example, legends and religion), thereby eliminating the chance of a coincidence that through blind luck both societies independently developed the same belief.[50] For our purposes here the Olmec civilization will be considered as represented by its successors the Aztec, Mayan, and Incan civilizations; these three combined as one group.

An outline of some of the everyday commonalities between the Old World and the New World will serve to show us that the three civilizations (that is, excluding the Indus) were much alike on a common everyday basis. Most commonalities are strictly a result of heritage and appear at the very inception of all three civilizations, a few result from natural progress and contact. Various scholars have compiled such lists but our purpose is to isolate certain items only for example and comment on their possible origin.[51]

1. **Mummification.** Very old. The style of practice varies but the practice was common to all three reemerging civilizations from the beginning.

2. **Head flattening.** Very old. Carried to extreme by the Maya. The practice continued to the near present in southern France and among the Basques.

3. **Tattoos.** Very old, but also widespread globally.

4. **Trepanning the skull.** (Removing part of the skull bone to relieve pressure.) Very old and a procedure requiring great skill.

5. **Making cotton cloth on the same type of loom in all three civilizations.** Very old. The citizens of the First Civilization wore cotton garments, not animal skins.

6. **Similarity of cotton clothing and of leather and fiber sandals.** Very old. Similarities between Sumer, Egypt, and Olmec-Aztec are amazing.

7. **Very similar ceramic items.** Similar designs and functions used for daily use, transport, and funeral ware. Very old.

8. **Metalwork.** Very old. All three civilizations used copper, tin, bronze, gold, and silver early on.

9. **Masonry and stonework.** Very old. Cement was ubiquitous, massive stone blocks cut, transported, and fitted.

10. **Divination.** Examining animal's entrails. Very old superstition.

11. **Witchcraft.** Very old. An interest of the common people not of the official religion.

12. **Oracles.** Very old. A huckster offshoot of the official religion accomplished by a priest. A type of fortune-telling.

13. **Wheel toys.** Very old. Found in both Mesoamerican (Olmec) and Mesopotamian tombs.

14. **Agriculture.** Irrigation, terrace farming, animal manure used by all three; similar farm tools.

15. **Dogs.** The only domestic animal common to both the Old World and New World is the dog. American dogs of 1492 strongly resemble Mesopotamian-Egyptian dogs.

16. **Measurements.** The Egyptian cubit was used as the unit of measurement in all the great structures of Mesoamerica. It is the only unit that works exactly for physical measurement of small and large units, and for mathematical ratios and square roots. (The cubit was based on the length of the arm from elbow to fingertip, about 18 inches. Its exact length varied from culture to culture.) Egyptian (First Civilization) finesse allowed 500 cubits to equal the distance the earth turns on the equator in one-half second of time. Both the Great Pyramid of Cheops in Egypt and the Sun Pyramid at Teotihuacán have bases that are 500 cubits per side. Thus, basic measurement evolves into architectural, astronomical and religious significance common to both civilizations. The Mayan civilization came long after the original Egyptian civilization had collapsed, yet used identical measurements and built the same kind of pyramids as Egypt's first pyramids. (Using these dates: Egyptian decline starts 2500 B.C., last pyramid built 1777 B.C., Teotihuacán's zenith A.D. 600. By this time the Egyptians did not know who built the Great Pyramid or what for, and they were incapable of telling anyone how to build a pyramid.) Contact seems an unlikely source for Mayan measurements, for by this time the Mesopotamian and Egyptian cultures were greatly in decline, pyramid building had long since ceased, and there is no evidence of exceptional astronomical or geophysical expertise in Egypt or Mesopotamia at this time. Heritage would be the prime cause of the measurement commonality; the subject matter is very old, too massive in content to be conveyed by causal contact, and the Mayan effort duplicates the First Civilization long

after the mideastern civilizations have failed and are not engaged in such works. In modern terms, there were no Egyptian tech reps available to help the Maya build pyramids.

The above sixteen items are but a token list of commonalities that in 1492 were found to exist between Mesoamerica and the early Mideast civilizations. The footnoted reference provides many more examples. As more items are added to the list the stronger the evidence of heritage becomes. Coincidence can only go so far before it becomes obvious that all three civilizations received the same stimulus from the First Civilization. This is why the everyday life of all three civilizations is so similar.

Three of the four reemerging civilizations (Sumer, Egypt, Olmec-Aztec but not Indus) exhibit striking commonalities in religion in their first days. The fantastic ideas that compose a packet of religious belief are not the products of natural progress. It would be impossible to accidentally duplicate the minute details of a given religion as religion springs entirely from human imagination. Neither is contact a possibility. From the earliest recorded ancient times (that is, the reemerging civilizations) mankind displayed a differential attitude toward other religions. It was a matter of interest only; there was no proselytizing, no religious wars, no heresies, and no inquisitions. All that came much later with the advent of monotheistic religions, particularly Christianity and Islam. The religions of these civilizations were indigenous; there was no transfer or foisting of one civilization's religion on another civilization. Heritage is the only explanation for the many religious commonalities, again for all three basic reasons: a) imaginative subject matter; b) there was too little time to gain such complexity; and c) it is unique and very old, pushing right up to "The Gap" at 5000 B.P. so we must assign a pre-10,500 B.P. date to its inception.

The three civilizations all worshiped the Sun. The ruler of each was a priest-king who was proclaimed a deity. The throne was "descended" from the sun. Pyramid complexes where priests lived were the centers of religion, where they performed ceremonies and collected exactions. All practiced human sacrifice for one or more religious objectives. And all believed in a glorious afterlife for royalty. As time went by the civilizations differentiated in the application of these concepts, but they remained in the same form to the end. Lest pages of text be consumed, suffice to say that man's religious inventory consists of thousands of disparate items of religious belief. Those stated above are a unique and singular group inherited from the First Civilization.

Religion permeated all three societies. In a very real way it was the glue that held them together. Because of it, the masses of common people were willing to support the extravagances of the ruler, his aristocracy and the legions of priests. They accepted being drafted to work on the construction of monumental structures of no practical value (to them) such as the pyramid complexes. Irrigation projects of obvious practical value to everyone did not need the impetus of religion to energize the workers, but it helped. For the ruling classes, religion served the purpose of disciplining the masses; it also organized them, kept them busy and subservient, gave the ruling class its luxury, security, and power to engage in miscellaneous wars. Because they arrived with religion in place the Sumerian, Egyptian, and Olmec-Aztec civilizations were able to rapidly progress, as they did.

Most of our knowledge of the religious practices of the earliest periods of these civilizations comes from the excavation of royal tombs. One text (The Age of God-Kings) describes the burial of members of the royal family at Ur, a Sumerian city-state (2550 B.C.) The burial location was a royal cemetery near the city's ziggurat. For one king's burial a great earthen pit was dug, a tomb chamber built, the ceremony completed, and the tomb was covered. The king was buried with the most valuable grave goods—gold, silver decorations, wardrobe chest—which represented a great deal of Ur's total wealth. Also in the pit were sixty-three bodies of attendants to the king. All of them had taken poison. This was necessary for the king to enjoy himself properly in the afterworld. Multiply this by hundreds of times over some centuries in one city-state and one can begin to comprehend the enormity of the grip that the priests had on the people.

The Egyptians began with royal burials similar to the Ur king's but rather quickly discarded the practice of human sacrifice. At Abydos (200 miles north of Luxor in central Egypt) archaeologists discovered the tombs of the kings and queens of the First Dynasty (3100 to 2800 B.C.) The pattern is the same as Ur's, exquisite grave goods, slaughtered servants and slaves. At the end of the First Dynasty the Egyptians developed the theory of substitution: paint pictures of grave goods, attendants, animals, boats, carriages, and the like on the walls of the tomb, and they will serve as the real things in the next world. (It was so because the priest said it was so, and it relieved a great burden on the treasury.) Nevertheless, wonderful grave goods were always buried with a royal personage.

Central America followed exactly the same pattern. The Mayan pyramids were funerary monuments with the burial chamber beneath, its entrance carefully concealed. The corpse would be accompanied by beautiful grave goods and sacrificial victims (men, women, and children). Human sacrifice was not restricted to royal burials. Its chief function was to propitiate the gods. This could mean seeking favors, as winning a war, but primarily to forestall the end of the world. The practice appeared in the earliest days of Sumer, Egypt, and Olmec-Aztec. We see the historical trail of the practice appearing most vividly in the Phoenicians of Biblical times and in the awful excesses of Native Americans of Cortés' time. Because of the experience of the devastation caused by the asteroid impact—which they assumed was the work of the gods punishing man—both the Phoenicians and the Central Americans practiced human sacrifice to forestall or prevent a repeat occurrence. The Phoenician beliefs are no surprise to Christians. The gods of the Old Testament are particularly bloodthirsty and require human sacrifice. Slaves would do but one's children were better. The ancient Jews sacrificed their children. The Carthaginians of 310 B.C. did the same for several centuries thereafter. In Central America, the Aztec slaughtered (and ate) fifty thousand people a year to forestall the end of the world. The Christian conquistadors practiced only symbolic cannibalism in communion. The real thing was quite barbaric.

In the Indus Valley we do not find the religious enthusiasm characteristic of the other three reemerging civilizations. Its workaday appearance hides the nature of whatever religious beliefs it had. This eastern demarcation line, which excluded the pyramids, also excludes the religion of the First Civilization. This is strong evidence that the First Civilization did not extend this far east. In all three of the reemerging civilizations one thing becomes quite clear: religion and science became mixed.

Scientific knowledge that had been saved from the First Civilization was jealously kept by the priests of the reemerging civilizations. The arrangement resembles the modern military's division into line and staff. Line fights the battles, staff supplies the line. The ruler and his aristocracy were line and ruled the country, but the priests were staff, perpetuated the fantastic religious beliefs and hoarded the considerable scientific knowledge inherited from the First Civilization. Thus, the grand accomplishments of these reemerging civilizations were made. But knowledge was secret, closely guarded and the key to priestly power. Therefore, it was easily lost. One war could do irreparable harm. The Spanish conquest would extinguish a civilization by eliminating the priests. In Egypt the seat of this concentration of knowledge was in the city of Heliopolis (east of Giza across the Nile). No such particular fount is known for Sumer or Mesoamerica.

CHAPTER 22: CULTURAL REMEMBRANCE OF THE ASTEROID

The ancients have repeatedly told us of the end of the First Civilization, that it ended in a worldwide catastrophe of earthquake, fire, and water. Some even knew the exact cause of the event, an asteroid strike, but most only know of the event, not its cause. The vehicles of transmission to us of the story are the myths, legends, and oral histories we have obtained from the archaeology of the reemerging civilizations. What are these? A myth is a story from imagination only, such as creation stories. Almost all religion is myth, often pure nonsense. A legend is a story based on historical fact but mixes in a fanciful story line of events and very often contains vivid mental pictures which are remarkably helpful in remembering the story. This is the very reason the story is told the way it is. Oral history is just that: a factual account of events remembered and passed on. Our admiration here goes to Herodotus (484– 424 (?) B.C.) who gathered information from many sources, oral and written, and produced a history of the ancient world remarkable for its accuracy and the first effort of its kind.

THEY CAME FROM THE EAST An inventory of the legends of American Indians shows one thing: they unanimously believe they came from the east. The Indians knew that their ancestors had crossed the ocean from the east and settled the Americas later to be visited by others who came from the east as witnessed by Montezuma's speech to Hernán Cortés in 1520.[52] The Mayan tradition was clear. They had come across the Atlantic led by Itzamna in a migration they called the "Great Arrival." The Maya know what they are talking about. In North America, the Micmacs and Algonquins have an oral history that their ancestors arrived by crossing the ocean from the east. Until 1819, they annually celebrated their safe arrival. Where they came from, or when they arrived, they did not know. The Mandans and Dakotas recalled their ancestors crossing the ocean for weeks in "huge skiffs." The Indians of the Great Lakes believe they came from the east. Hopi tradition recounts an arrival from the tropical south after crossing the ocean on huge reed (!) rafts. The Aztec and Toltec say their ancestors came from the east, as do the Indians of Brazil. Legends of eastern origins are recorded in religious books of Central America. The *Popol Vuh*, the sacred book of the Quiché Indians of central Mexico, records that "they pulled up stakes there and left the east . . . from that great distance." The books of Chilam Balam, a Mayan work, report the first arrivals to have come from across the sea, originally landing on the island of Cozumel off the coast of Yucatán. These books were manuscripts of Mayan legends written down after the Spanish Conquest by Mayan natives at the request of and with the help of certain enlightened friars. One of the authors validates his work by stating:

> I, Don Francisco Gómez, first Ahzib Quiché, write here
> on this paper of the coming of our fathers and grandfathers
> from the other side of the sea whence the sun rises.
> *(Popol Vuh, p.14)*

Significantly, there is not a single mention in any American Indian legend of their ancestors arriving in the Americas after walking south through 3,000 miles of ice. It never happened.

THE FLOOD After they arrived, disaster struck. An unmitigated catastrophe impacted all mankind. It was sudden, malevolent, overwhelming, and total. It nearly eradicated man. The legends of this event are worldwide, yet remarkably uniform in the telling. We can call it "The Flood" for convenience, a reference to the biblical deluge which of course was the asteroid impact of 10,500 B.P. The Flood legends are old. They immediately appear with the reemerging civilizations. The newly arrived Sumerians (5000 B.P.) had a full account of the flood that destroyed the world. The hero of the story, Utnapishtin, was warned in advance by a god, Ea, to build a boat and "put aboard the seed of all living things," which he did. The end of the tempest was determined by releasing a raven that did not return. Utnapishtin survived and repopulated the world. We immediately note the similarity to the story of Noah's flood, which is a historical derivative of the Sumerian legend. The Sumerian legend was transported to Palestine by Abraham, who left Ur in 4100 B.P. and walked with his tribe into Palestine. The tribe retained the legend, but over time, and through priestly revisionism incorporated it into their own folklore and renamed the hero Noah, one of their own.

In *Fingerprints of the Gods,* Graham Hancock accomplished a tour de force of cataloging the world's flood legends (p. 187–199). Here is a brief summary of that work. Over 500 Flood legends are known around the world. The German scholar Dr. Richard Andree concluded that sixty-two were entirely independent of the Mesopotamian and Hebrew traditions. The Flood story is found in the legends of Indians of the Americas. In North America, the legend is held by the Inuit of Alaska, the Luiseno of lower California, the Huron of the Great Lakes, the Algonquin and Iroquis of the east, and Chickasaw and Sioux of the center. In Central America the legend is told by the Olmec, the Aztec and Maya, and it is recorded in the holy book of *Popol Vuh.* In South America: by the Chiba of Columbia, the Canarian of Ecuador, the Tupinamba of Brazil, the Inca of Peru (the Andes), Araucnaian of Chile, and the Yamana of Tierra del Fuego. Worldwide, the Flood legend is found in Malaysia, Laos, Thailand, Burma, Vietnam, Australia, Japan, Hawaii, Samoa, Greece, India, and Egypt in the *Book of the Dead.* Invariably the reason for the catastrophe is the gods' displeasure with man. In many cases man is saved by one man riding out the tempest in a ship, often accompanied by all living things.

The Sumerian legend of the Flood has found unique confirmation in Ur. In 1929, while excavating at Ur, Sir Leonard Wooley had already reached a depth of 40 feet when he struck a layer of clay 8 feet thick. The 40 feet already excavated yielded artifacts of a purely Sumerian civilization. The 8 feet of clay was clean with no artifacts. Below the clay were artifacts of a mixed culture, partly Sumerian and partly something else. Thus, Ur provides the clay of the Flood. The ziggurat at Nippur, a nearby Sumerian city, provided an ancient library of 35,000 clay tablets. One of these contained the original Sumerian version of the Flood.

THE ASTEROID The Flood legends account for the catastrophe by saying that the gods were displeased with mankind; however, in most cases the victims were ignorant of its physical cause. A few people of the world knew the cause of the catastrophe was the fall of a heavenly body to earth. Undoubtedly, they saw the bolide with their own eyes. This information was passed on in the form of a legend just like the story of the Flood. Central America would be the best vantage point from which to view the passage of the asteroid on its track from south of Alaska to the mid-Atlantic Ocean. The falling asteroid would look just as the natives of Central America have described it—a Feathered Serpent. This was discussed in "Part IV: The Asteroid." The motif of the Feathered Serpent permeates Central American religion. We also find this motif in paintings, architecture, and costumes. It also has a practical function, as we shall see, the start of the Mayan calendar. The Central American natives who witnessed "The Feathered Serpent that Fell from the Sky" well knew that it was a heavenly body, and that it was the cause of the ensuing disaster. In *The Books of Chilam Balam* (the creation story of the Mayas of the Yucatán peninsula) it states:

> Ah Mucencab came forth and obscured the face of the Heavens . . . the earth began to awaken. Nobody knew what was to come. Suddenly subterranean fires burst forth into the Sky, and fire rained down from above, and ashes descended, and rocks and trees were thrown down, and wood and stone smashed together.
>
> Then the Heavens were seized and split asunder. The face of the Heavens was buffeted to and fro and thrown on its back . . . (the people) were all torn to pieces; their hearts failed them while they yet lived. Then they were buried in the sands, in the sea.
>
> In one great sudden rush of water the Great Serpent was ravished from the Heavens. The Sky fell and the earth sank, and the four gods, the Bacabs, arose who brought about the destruction of the world.

This is *not* the description of a normal catastrophic storm like a hurricane or tornado. The legend in fact describes what really happened, a celestial body fell from the sky (the Feathered Serpent), hit the ocean, caused immense tidal waves, volcanism, fire in the sky, immeasurable wind, and asphyxiating gases. The stars moved; it poured rain and volcanic ash. The very legend recognizes an exceptional event. Compare the legend to a brief description of the destruction of St. Pierre by Mount Pelee in 1902:

The death and destruction appeared to be entirely the work of the volcanic cloud, formed of superheated steam and other gases made heavy by billions of particles of incandescent ash and traveling with enough force to carry along boulders and blocks of volcanic material. At the rum distillery, the burned-out tanks, massive containers of quarter-inch boiler plate riveted together, looked to Hovey 'as if they had been through a bombardment by artillery, being full of holes which vary in size from mere cracks at the bottom of indentations to great rents, 34, 30 and even 36 inches across.'
(Dr. William Melson, *Planet Earth Volcano,* p. 33)

Sifting through the wreckage and examining the evidence, the scientists concluded that the temperature of the incandescent cloud had been between 1,300° and 1,800°F, enough to soften glass (1,292°F) but not enough to melt copper (1,981°F). Copper telephone wires were found intact, not fused together. As it swept through St. Pierre, the cloud had annihilated the people by both blast and heat, doing its work in a few moments. Many corpses were torn apart and others dreadfully burned. A reporter who ventured into the still smoldering city found "an open and comparatively smooth stretch of ground strewn with hundreds of dead bodies. Not a shred of clothing was upon any of them, not a single hair."

An architectural example of the Feathered Serpent that fell from the sky is to be seen at Chichén Itzá, Yucatán, Mexico. On the northernmost staircase, at the spring and autumn equinox, shadows create a giant serpent coming downward toward the ground where the sides of the staircase end in the heads of large serpents. Mayan art often marks the Sky Serpent with the signs for the Sun, Moon, Venus, and other celestial bodies.

In another world far away, a legend of the asteroid fall is kept. The legend of Atlantis is the story of an island in the Atlantic that sunk in a single day. We have the story because it was written down by Plato (428–347 B.C.) at a gathering where his maternal uncle Critias the Younger repeats a story told by an Egyptian priest of Sais (near Alexandria, Nile Delta) to Critias' ancestor Solon (630–560 B.C.). The introductory remarks of the priest draw our attention.

[M]any have been the destruction of mankind, and many shall be. The greatest are by fire and by water, but besides

John Cogan

these there are lesser ones. For, indeed, the tale that is also told among you, how that Phaethon yoked his father's chariot, and, for that he could not drive in his father's path, he burnt up all things upon earth and was himself smitten by a thunderbolt and slain; this story has the air of a fable; but the truth concerning it is related to a *deviation of the bodies that move round the earth in the heavens*, whereby at long intervals of time a destruction through fire of the things that are upon earth occurs. (italics added for emphasis)[53]

The story goes on, but the point has been made: it was an asteroid impact that caused the destruction of Atlantis along with that of almost all mankind.

Two other legends tell of the asteroid's fall in a very positive way. Unlike the Mayan legend and Plato's story, it was not visually observed. In these legends, far from the point of impact, the teller informs us of the Sun, Moon, and stars moving. It was the earth that moved as a result of the asteroid impact but to a faraway observer the appearance would be that the heavens moved not the earth. But the catastrophic tidal waves and the monstrous cloud of death quickly arrived. The ancients were well aware it was one event. An ancient Scandinavian legend, the *Voluspa*, recites in verse four:

> From the south the sun, the moon's companion,
> touched the edge of the heavens.
> The sun did not know his halls.
> The moon did not know her might
> The stars did not know their places.
> (Otto Muck, *The Secret of Atlantis*, p. 176)

A Chinese legend of ancient date recounts:

> [W]hen mankind rebelled again at the high gods and the system of the universe fell into disorder: The planets altered their courses. The sky sank lower towards the north. The sun, moon and stars changed their motions. The earth fell to pieces and the waters in its bosom rushed upwards with violence and overflowed the earth.
> (Graham Hancock, *Fingerprints of the Gods*, p. 193)

There are many other legends that recount the asteroid's fall. Egyptian legend says that it was "the eye of Ra" that fell into the sea and caused the destruction of mankind. The Bella Coola Indians of Canadian British Columbia have Father Sun, who hurls his offspring to earth in anger. The Algonquin Indians of eastern North America have a god who throws himself into the sea, causing it to flood the earth. Both the Bella Coola and Algonquin Indians were under the flight path of the asteroid.

THE MAYAN CALENDAR The Mayan calendar is so accurate that it is one of man's outstanding inventions. It is based on the pure science of celestial revolutions. It is not a legend. Why include it in our discussion of legends? Because the Mayan calendar starts on the day of the fall of the asteroid and the consequent flood. Legends give us our cultural knowledge of these events. The Mayan calendar uses this as its start; it, therefore, dates for us the exact time of the asteroid impact and the end of the First Civilization.

The Maya were absolutely obsessed with time. The façades of all their structures were covered with hieroglyphics at first indecipherable. Scholars finally realized they were calendar dates, a great architectural memorial to the passage of time. All over Central America, every fifty-two years, a new perimeter was built around the temple mounds (the fifty-two-year cycle was of great age and called a Calendar Round). Exactly why this time period was chosen is unknown. In *The Maya*, author Michael D. Coe describes the Maya fixation as follows:

> Every single Maya ritual act was dictated by the calendar, above all by the 260 day count. These sacred performances were imbued with symbolic meaning. For instance, the number 4, 9, and 13 and the colour directions appear repeatedly. Before and during rituals food taboos and sexual abstinence were rigidly observed, and self mutilation was carried out by jabbing needles and sting ray spines through ears, cheeks, lips, tongue, and the penis, the blood being spattered on paper or used to anoint the idols. On the eve of the Conquest such idols were censed with copal and rubber as well as ritually fed. Human sacrifice was perpetrated on prisoners, slaves, and above all on children (bastards or orphans bought for the occasion). Nevertheless, before the Toltec era, animals rather

than people may have been the more common victims, and we know that such creatures as wild turkeys, dogs, squirrels, quail, and iguanas were considered fit offerings for the Maya gods.

(Michael D. Coe, *The Maya*, p. 154)

Other authors have seriously questioned whether insanity of a sort was involved. But the reason behind the calendar obsession was exactly the same reason that was behind massive human sacrifice—to appease the gods, and thus forestall the end of the world. In other words, avoid a repeat of the catastrophe memorialized in their calendar and rituals.

The finest explanation of the Mayan calendar ever written is Otto Muck's, *The Secret of Atlantis* (p. 241–255). However, the reader is warned. It is technical and very difficult reading. Muck is an expert on calendar matters having previously written an analysis of the Egyptian Sothis calendar. Michael D. Coe's effort, *The Maya*, is also worthy (p. 149). There are many more. One overwhelming fact stands out: the calendar is immensely old. An analysis of the working of the calendar requires that the heavens be critically observed (and recorded) for millennia before 10,500 B.P. Modern astronomers have telescopes, clocks, instruments to measure minute angles, and the ability to make lengthy mathematical calculations. All this allows them to calculate orbits and planetary motions after a few centuries of observation. The Maya, inheritors from the First Civilization, would have required thousands of years of observation (in lieu of instruments) to attain the calendar's great accuracy. Readings from the inscriptions at Palenque show that the Maya knew the earth's sidereal year (one revolution about the Sun, Maya calculation 365.242129 days; actual 365.25636 days); the synodical revolutions of the planet Jupiter (a correlation between Earth's revolutions around the Sun and Jupiter, Earth 3,001 revolutions—one revolution being one year—and Jupiter 2,748 and the conjunction Sun-Earth-Jupiter is repeated); the synodical revolutions of the planet Mars (Earth 3,803, Mars 1,781). Only by observing these planetary motions through several cycles can we achieve such accuracy. Jupiter would require six thousand years for two cycles. The Maya also knew the periodicity of the planet Venus and the Moon so well that they were utilized to check their basic calendar.

The Gregorian calendar is expressed in years, months and days, the

Mayan in *baktun* ("long count" of 144,000 days) and *haab* (fifty-two years). The Mayan calendar had a correction cycle which was independent of the basic calendar (that is, the 260-day *tzolkin* based on the Moon, eclipses and the phases of Venus). If we take any day—today, for instance—and work backward through the Mayan calendar, there is one day when the three counts come together: June 4, 8498 B.C. We may refer to this as the beginning of the Mayan calendar. It is a beginning in numbers, but is it also the date of an event worthy of the start of a calendar? Christians date the Gregorian calendar from the birth of Jesus; Mohammedans from Mohammed's flight from Mecca to Medina; Romans from the foundation of Rome; Jews from the date of creation. There was an attempt in France to start a calendar based on the fall of the Bastille called the French Republican calendar, but it was short lived. In 1929, the U.S.S.R. proposed a Revolutionary calendar but it was not used. The Maya record the event of the asteroid fall. From that day on this obsession with time began.

In other literature discussing the origin of the Mayan calendar the date of 3113 B.C. is often given as the year of its start. This is not the start of the Mayan calendar; it is its first anniversary. Muck would place the first anniversary at 3373 B.C. On this day the three chronological elements of the calendar came together again just the same as at the true beginning of the calendar in 8498 B.C. The date of 8498 B.C. was the date of the Venus-Moon-Earth conjunction and the date of the fall of the asteroid with its catastrophe for mankind. This was an event well worth starting a new calendar. In 3113 B.C. nothing of note happened, hardly a day to start a calendar. Further, the Mayans have all sorts of references to dates well before 3113 B.C. Their astronomy predates that date by well over 10,000 years.

THE LEGEND OF ATLANTIS This subject has attracted so much silliness that its basic value to history has been obscured. A brass-tack approach is required. Reference to Atlantis as a disappeared land, an island, is worldwide and the accounts are independent. It is often part and parcel of the legend of the Flood which makes the legend of Atlantis itself as old as the legends of the Flood. The account of the destruction of Atlantis given by Plato is only one infinitely small piece of the worldwide legends of Atlantis, just as the story of Noah is only one small piece of the worldwide legends of the Flood.

Let us take a quick look at some of the legends of Atlantis, the disappeared land. In Wales and Ireland quite colorful ancient legends tell of people coming from a now submerged land. The Romans recorded Gallic and Celtic legends of people coming from a sunken island. The Berber Tribes of North Africa recall warlike people from a submerged island in the Atlantic. The Basques of the Pyrenees Mountains believe they are descendants of a sunken island called Atlantis. The original (circa A.D. 1395) Canary Islanders trace their origins to a sunken island catastrophe. Their myth holds that they were the only survivors. Farther east (Egypt, Babylonia, and India) the legends become more general and vague but refer to a mystical land in the ocean to the west. It is in the Americas that the legend of sunken Atlantis is vividly alive. We have above noted under the caption "They Came From The East," that tribes of North, Central, and South America have legends that they crossed the ocean and came from the east. Some of the legends have the embellishment that they came from a now sunken land (for example, Aztec). The division probably does reflect reality; most came from North Africa, some from a now sunken land. Noteworthy also are the derivatives of the word Atlantis frequently found in the New World: Antilla (island); Aztlan (Aztec name for a sunken island in the Atlantic Ocean); and Azatlan (word for city, Mexico). In the Old World there are also some striking similarities: Attala (Berber name of sunken island); Avalon (Irish, Welch, Celtic name for Atlantis); and Atalaya (Canary Island name for Atlantis). Richard Wingate points out that ancient authors often referred to a lost Atlantis. Herodotus is notable for this and obtained his information from Egyptian priests, as Solon had some years earlier (Herodotus 500 B.C.; Solon 600 B.C.).

Plato's tale of Atlantis is of special consideration due to its clarity. Plato merely recorded the telling of the story by Critias the Younger (his maternal uncle) at a festival (380 B.C.?) of a few intellectuals at Piracus, Greece. Socrates, that world-class cynic, was one (of probably four) in attendance. According to Critias, his ancestor, Solon (630–560 B.C.), had been told the story by an Egyptian priest at Sais, Egypt. Solon, in retelling the story, had said that it was "strange but true." Socrates, quoted by Plato, eased Critias' mind and said he and the others would accept it as true (the festival required that the stories be truthful). Critias then tells the story of a prosperous island past Gibraltar (the Pillars of Hercules) in the Atlantic whose people rule North Africa, wage war on the Greeks and Egyptians but are defeated. Immediately thereafter, a natural catastrophe destroys the three armies and the Atlantic island sinks into the sea. The story was dated by the Egyptian priest at 8,000 years before Solon's visit to Egypt (that is, 8560 B.C. Gregorian).

Another point of the tale is remarkable. It says the inhabitants of Atlantis sailed "to the whole continent on the other side." Something no Greek of Plato's day knew anything about. The story also pinpoints the location of Atlantis—the Azores. This was hard to believe only until 1872 when the research vessel *Challenger* discovered the Azores Plateau, a landmass of 154,400 square miles, 10,000 feet below sea level, which contained the nine mountains peaks (constituting the present Azores Islands) and a huge plain of one-half the total landmass (77,000 square miles). (It is precisely here that the Gulf Stream crosses the Mid-Atlantic Ridge, of which the Azores Plateau is a part, and continues northeastward to Europe.) The Azores Plateau is the only location in the North Atlantic near the Pillars of Hercules that fits Plato's description. And there is convincing evidence that it was above sea level during the last Ice Age.

Given the date of 10,500 B.P. (that is, 8500 B.C.) for the denouement of Plato's Atlantis let us quickly review the world situation at that time. Ice-age aridity is at its peak. The Sahara has been drying up since before glacial maximum (18,000 B.P.); that is, since 40,000 B.P., and there is no arable land left. The population has been emigrating for ten thousand years to the north (Europe), the west (the Americas), and to the east, but now in the east are two nation-states barring newcomers. This served as a perfect excuse for war between the island state, its western North African hegemony on one hand and Greco-Egyptian hegemony on the other. Immediately following the triumph by the Greeks and Egyptians the asteroid fell destroying the three armies and most of the rest of the world in the Atlantic catastrophe.

We want to note that Homo sapiens became civilized in North Africa and spread throughout the world in great part by ship. This colonized the island of Atlantis itself, but when? A good guess would be when Homo sapiens first entered Europe from the west by ship. This can be measured by the inception of the art caves at 34,000 B.P. The first settlers probably arrived in Atlantis between 40,000 and 34,000 B.P. If, however, this stretches credibility as being too early, we can note that 80 percent of the art in these caves appeared from 15,000 to 10,500 B.P. At the same time, man was crossing the Atlantic and settling the New World.

Atlantis could certainly have been colonized during this time. If Plato's story is correct, it was well before 10,500 B.P.

Plato's description of the country of Atlantis, its city, royal palace, oceangoing ships, canals, military forces, and the like is a description very familiar to us. It is a description of a high Stone Age civilization and is almost a mirror image of the Mesopotamian, Egyptian, and Central American reemerging civilizations at their peak. If we wish to embrace the legend totally, it could be a partial description of the First Civilization.

Now a disclaimer. The evidence of the First Civilization is complete with or without the legend of Atlantis. But the legend of Atlantis fits in perfectly with the concept of civilized man spreading throughout the world, adding weight on the side of the legend being true. Further, placing the legend in the perspective of the world scene at the time makes it a commonplace of history and not at all an exaggeration as its detractors purport it to be.

Thus, the legends of the world well document the fact that the American Indians came from the east across the ocean to the New World, that a catastrophe occurred that nearly destroyed mankind, and the cause of it was a falling heavenly body. The event is well dated. Plato's legend dates it; the Mayan calendar dates it; and modern science has dated it, twice. It was first dated by the Greenland ice core which contains the detritus of the asteroid impact (ash, carbon dioxide, sea salts) at a precise level; and the second time through carbon dating by determining the date of the end of all work in 200 art caves in Europe. All sources confirm that the catastrophe occurred 10,500 years ago.

Part VI: Conclusion

CHAPTER 23: SUMMARY

A summary of the most important facts from the prior chapters will provide a working base from which we can advance to compare the New Order of paleohistory with the Old Order and set our sights on better organization and presentation of paleohistory. It will also help to identify the voids in our knowledge of paleohistory so that archaeology, at last, will have proper focus and direction in its efforts to expose the past. The first step is to introduce a calendar of the New Order for convenience and provide a summarized chronology. (See end of this chapter.)

The universe is the product of the big bang, which occurred 15 billion years ago and is still in progress. Our solar system is the product of a supernova explosion and is 5 billion years old. The Sun and nine planets formed from the debris of the supernova explosion through the action of gravity and the process of agglomeration, which entailed numerous and massive interstellar collisions. The number of these collisions was greater during the first part of the solar system's formation and crater remains are easily seen on Mars and the Moon. The Moon displays some 30,000 impacts remaining on its near side, but due to the effects of erosion and water activity, Earth shows only 200 craters. The incidence of earth impact by interplanetary objects is now greatly reduced but is still a very real and present danger to life on earth. It is said by astronomers that Earth exists in a swarm of asteroids. Particularly worrisome is the asteroid belt between Mars and Jupiter where a collision between asteroids or a perturbation by Jupiter could send an unknown asteroid on a collision pathway with Earth. Other families of asteroids independent of the asteroid belt have orbits near Earth. One of these, the Adonis group, is suspected of spawning the asteroid that hit the earth 10,500 years ago in the Atlantic Ocean.

The impact created gigantic and worldwide tsunamis hundreds of feet high, opened all fracture lines in the Atlantic seabed and activated all volcanic vents throughout the Atlantic. The explosions continued for several days and created a continental size cloud of incredible violence, winds of hundreds of miles per hour, and enough heat to melt glass. The cloud was filled with asphyxiating gas, contained $^1/_{10}$ of the water from the North Atlantic, debris from its seabed and volcanic ash. The cloud drifted with the prevailing winds both east and west. It poured a mud-filled rain over Europe and Asia. The loess soil belt is the mark of its path toward the east. In the east, it began to curve toward the north and here lie the bodies of millions of quick-frozen woolly mammoths. The bones of millions of smaller animals were washed by the rain into massive piles. Thus the asteroid has left a chain of proof of its impact. It starts with the 3,000 Carolina Bays; the two Atlantic seafloor craters, the Atlantic seafloor sediments that show current drift toward the Mid-Atlantic Ridge; evidence of quick subsidence of a great part of the North Atlantic Basin; the 5,000-mile loess belt stretching from Europe to China; and the huge piles of fossil bones in the Siberian Arctic.

The cloud passed directly overland, extinguishing all life by asphyxiation, violence and mud rain. Toxic gasses released by volcanism in both the Northern and Southern Hemispheres almost eliminated the ozone layer that protects the earth from the solar ultraviolet radiation. This radiation caused the sterilization of large, open country dwelling animals and the extinction of over half of such species worldwide. The gyroscopic oscillation of the earth after the impact perturbed the protective Van Allen radioactive belts and allowed cosmic hard particle radiation to reach the earth in large amounts causing a great increase in harmful mutations to all living things. This was a secondary cause of the great extinctions.

The asteroid hit at the end of the Ice Age. Unfortunately for modern science, the end of the Ice Age has had the effect of masking the event of the asteroid impact. But the physical facts, as stated above, are clear and modern science has further corroborated the impact. The impact caused the, otherwise inexplicable, rapid melt of ice-age glaciers due to a worldwide instantaneous temperature rise. Scientists have since discovered that ice cores taken in Greenland from 10,500 B.P. show an instantaneous rise of 20°F (11°C) in the earth's atmosphere and contain massive amounts of carbon dioxide, volcanic ash and copious sea salt. We can readily date the time of the impact at 10,500 B.P. using these

Greenland ice cores and other evidence such as the end of work in two hundred art caves, the beginning of the Mayan calendar and even Plato's story of Atlantis.

When the Ice Age ended (the melt occurred between 10,500 and 6,500 B.P.) glacial maximum had passed (at 18,000 B.P.), but because of ecological inertia little had changed by 10,500 B.P. Ice and permafrost covered one-third of the earth's landmass. Another one-third had become desert through the Ice Age phenomenon of aridity. The Ice Age period was from 117,000 to 10,500 B.P. Glaciation and aridity were progressive throughout this period. Human life on earth was confined to the "wet spots" of the tropics. From 40,000 to 10,500 B.P., North African man searched the world for places to live.

Man had developed through evolution in Africa and had reached the present modern level of physical and intellectual development 150,000 years ago. His homeland was North Africa now the Sahara desert (^{1}/16 of the landmass of the world), which during the first part of the last Ice Age was an excellent habitat for early man with plentiful game, rivers, lakes, and savanna ecology. Homo sapiens multiplied greatly and by 40,000 B.P., these humans had begun a civilization, which by 10,500 B.P. reached a high stone-age level equivalent to or superior to that of the Indus, Mesopotamian, Egyptian, and Central American empires in their prime. It was a maritime civilization of worldwide import. Physical and cultural evidence of this civilization remains in the form of ship design, maps, architectural remnants on land and below sea level, cultural and scientific knowledge, astronomy, architecture, religious beliefs, and legends of the civilization's spread and fall due to the asteroid impact. Heritage from the First Civilization explains the simultaneous rise of four independent civilizations five thousand years after the asteroid impact. The Indus, but particularly the Mesopotamian, Egyptian, and Central American civilizations all appeared suddenly, spontaneously, in full flower absent of any evidence of historical progress, and the originators of each all came from somewhere else.

Striking similarities unite these civilizations. Furthermore, these similarities confirm their common heritage from the First Civilization. In fact, the cities of these reemerging civilizations show us what those of the First Civilization looked like. This was forcefully impressed on all scholars from 1492 to the present when the connection between the Old World and the New World, lost since 10,500 B.P., was reestablished. To the amazement of the Europeans, the two American continents were found fully settled with 42 million Native Americans and in Central America a high Stone Age civilization still intact which greatly resembled those of Egypt and Mesopotamia at 5,000 B.P. Legends from both the Old World and the New World recall the First Civilization and the cosmic catastrophe. These reemerging civilizations are the perfect picture of man recovering from the catastrophe of the asteroid impact and resuming the First Civilization. It is exactly what one would expect to happen.

Some lingering historical questions are now easy to answer. For example, the cause of the great megafauna extinction of 10,500 B.P. was the loss of the ozone layer and the Van Allen radiation belts; and, the New World was populated by humans who fled the increasing aridity of the Sahara by using boats and rafts to follow the Canary Current to the Americas, principally South America. The asteroid impact ended communication between the Old and New Worlds, which was not reestablished until A.D. 1492 (except for occasional trading voyages).

With the calendar of *The New Order of Man's History* and the above summary in mind, let us now engage in some freethinking employing a mixture of scientific discipline and our best mental efforts at deduction when pertinent factual data is absent.

CALENDAR OF THE NEW ORDER OF MAN'S HISTORY

CT boundary. Asteroid impact ends the Age of dinosaurs and begins the age of mammals	65 million B.P.
Australopithecus (Lucy)	3 million–1.6 million B.P.
Homo erectus (Turkana Boy)	2 million–150,000 B.P.
Neanderthal (Europe)	200,000–20,000 B.P.
Homo sapiens	150,000–present
Cro-Magnon (Europe)	40,000–10,500 B.P.
The Last Ice Age	117,000–10,500 B.P.
Sahara Dries Up	40,000–10,500 B.P.
The First Civilization	40,000–10,500 B.P.
Europe Settled	40,000–10,500 B.P.
Art Caves	34,000–10,500 B.P.
The New World Settled	20,000–10,500 B.P.
World is Mapped	20,000–10,500 B.P.
Glacial Maximum	18,000 B.P.
Period of Mass Emigration from North Africa	15,000–10,500 B.P.
Clovis Lithic Culture (Americas)	12,000–10,500 B.P.
Asteroid Impact	10,500 B.P.
End of Ice Age (The Melt)	10,500–6,500 B.P.
Contact Lost: The Old World-The New World	10,500 B.P.
The Great Extinction	10,500 B.P.
The Oceans Rise	10,500–6,500 B.P.
Beginning of Mayan Calendar	10,500 B.P.
"The Gap" (Mesolithic Age)	10,500–5,000 B.P.
Man Recovers (Reemerging Civilizations)	5,000–present
Contact Renewed: The Old World-The New World	A.D. 1492
Man Discovers the Ice Ages (L. Agassiz)	A.D. 1840
Man Discovers His Ancestors (C. Darwin: Origin of Species)	A.D. 1859
Man Discovers the Asteroid Impact (O. Muck)	A.D. 1965
Camp Century Greenland Ice Core	A.D. 1985

CHAPTER 24: SPECULATION AND COMMENT

In our text we started with an examination of the Ice Age itself and reviewed the evolutionary passage of man from animal to human and the rise of the First Civilization. We then analyzed its destruction by an asteroid, an event contemporaneous with the end of the last Ice Age. This was followed by a description of man's recovery from the catastrophe. This history of man is called the New Order. It is a long and complex story impossible to tell in particularity and in its entirety. This text must of necessity be an outline of these events. It is to be hoped that more and more of the missing parts of man's saga will be filled in by science. Some questions stand out and need to be addressed, even if our only method of research is reason and scientific speculation. A working hypothesis is essential to all scientific advancement.

Our first question is geophysical. When the asteroid impacted the earth, did it permanently change the angle of its axis of rotation as to the ecliptic and/or did the crust of the earth move forward in the direction of the asteroid's flight path? Both assumptions are correct. The axis of rotation and the crust of the earth both moved toward the asteroid's point of impact. The first fact of our investigation must be our own realization that this is not an "earthly" event. The impact of a $6^{1}/_{4}$ mile diameter asteroid traveling 43,000 miles per hour striking the planet Earth is a cosmic event; the consequences will be massive, unusual and unique. Terrestrial tidal waves, volcanic action, and earthquakes have nothing in common quantitatively with such an event. It has been argued previously that the earth's axis of rotation tipped in a line toward the point of the asteroid impact. Exactly how far it tipped, we do not know, but this geophysical effect is accompanied by another geophysical effect at once more complex yet more measurable—the movement of the earth's crust over the liquid mantle it rests upon.

For simplicity's sake, we can visualize the earth as a three-piece object. It is a nickel iron-core surrounded by liquid magma and topped with a crust, which varies from 9 miles thick in the North Atlantic to 25 miles thick under the continents. The crust moves about slowly and ponderously on the liquid magma. This activity is plate tectonics. But could it possibly move quickly? Otto Muck says it can and in fact did so upon the asteroid's impact. Two other luminaries of science back him up, Charles H. Hapgood and Albert Einstein. In *Earth's Shifting Crust*, Professor Hapgood concludes that the ice caps in the earth's Northern and Southern Hemispheres have an impulse (centrifugal force) to move toward the equator because of the axial spinning of the earth and their asymmetrical placement (that is, not placed at the North or South Pole axis of rotation). Albert Einstein wrote a preface to the book saying that the theory was perfectly sound.[54]

Muck, Hapgood, and Einstein are not to be lightly dismissed. They score a bull's-eye because both forces did in fact combine to move the earth's crust when the asteroid struck. The asteroid came in low and fast (30° angle to Earth 43,000 miles per hour) at an angle of 40° to the equator—a perfect tangential approach to move the earth's crust (as opposed to a straight penetration). The earth had accumulated a maximum amount of ice because there had been very little melting between glacial maximum at 18,000 and 10,500 B.P. at the time of impact. The vast majority of ice was in North America, one-third as much in Europe. There was relatively little in the Southern Hemisphere, except for the massive accumulation of ice in Antarctica. This made the point of impact southeast of the North American ice sheet absolutely perfect to do the job of moving the earth's crust. The direction of the crustal movement was along the flight path of the asteroid. This path is easy to discern—just draw a line from Charlestown, South Carolina to the impact crater. The pathway will also occur along a line that encircles the earth. But there is no crustal movement 90° east and west of this line.[55] If we apply this to the earth we see that North America would drop toward the equator along the force line and Siberia would rise toward the Arctic (Siberia is exactly opposite the point of impact). Next, we must confront the question of how the millions of woolly mammoths of Siberia were fast-frozen, preserving their meat in edible condition for 10,000 years. We know that they died and were covered with mud as a result of the death cloud that emanated from the Atlantic catastrophe, but why and how they froze is a separate and singular mystery. Any and all suggested solutions are welcome—but only one works: the crust of the earth moved as a result of the forces of the asteroid impact and the impulse of the North American ice sheet toward the equator and this movement carried the Siberian behemoths 1,500 miles north into the Arctic Circle. The distance is estimated by measuring the present distance south to a type of habitat and environment the mammoths lived in at their death. They did not live in snow and ice; each adult mammoth required 400 pounds of food per day which is only available in a cold-temperate climate with plenty of grass and trees—not the barren snow- and ice-covered tundra (of no nutritional value) where they are found today. So they were moved to where they are now found. Weather change cannot be an explanation. These animals were fast-frozen. This is why they are intact. A weather change would take too long, and the carcasses would putrify long before they froze. And there is no evidence of a weather change. At the latitude of the Arctic Circle where the frozen mammoths are now found, it was always fiercely cold through the Pleistocene. The habitat was ice and snow-covered tundra; mammoths could not have lived in such conditions. Neither could the millions of other animals that lived alongside the mammoths endure the present arctic habitat where their disarticulated bones are now found in massive piles, having been washed there by the catastrophic rains of the death cloud. We conclude that as a result of the asteroid impact the earth's crust moved, and its axial tilt slightly increased.

Our second question is how to best describe the First Civilization? Its physical and cultural remnants have been previously described, but these are fractional and do not give us a clear picture of what the First Civilization was like. Of course we will never know about it in detail because of its almost complete destruction physically and culturally. Four forces have been at work to destroy the evidence of the First Civilization: 1) the asteroid impact; 2) the end of the Ice Age; 3) the destruction of real and personal property and of written and oral records by man himself; and 4) the present fragmentation of a formerly homogeneous human population.

1. **The asteroid impact.** It is impossible to find any better angle of aim or point of impact to do maximum damage to the earth than was done by Asteroid A (Muck's term) at 10,500 B.P. Man

was confined to the tropics by the Ice Age because of the ice and permafrost. Aridity caused desertification. His strongholds were North Africa, Eurasia to the east along the tropic of Cancer and Central America. The asteroid targeted this area. The tsunamis, earthquakes and death cloud destroyed all things. Very little survived.[56]

2. **The end of the Ice Age.** Beginning at 10,500 B.P. the great melt began and the North American and European ice sheets were gone by 6500 B.P. The world was awash with water. North America was covered with immense lakes and today's Canada was almost nonexistent. The oceans rose 400 feet during the melt, covering with water whatever evidence remained after the asteroid impact of man's prior occupation.

3. **The destruction of evidence of the First Civilization by man himself.** For the moment reference here is only to written records. The topic is very well expressed by Richard Wingate in *Lost Outpost of Atlantis* (p. 144–148). A brief summary of his work follows. Throughout historical times it has been rather commonplace for men to intentionally destroy the records of themselves or others for political or religious reasons. Medieval Christians worked hard in this regard. They destroyed ancient Anglo-Saxon literature so thoroughly that only one poem, *Beowulf*, survives. "Gleeful Irish Monks destroyed ten thousand books written in ancient runic script on birch bark in a single bonfire in Ireland." The Catholic Inquisition (after the Romans) attacked the Druidic libraries destroying everything. In the New World the same pattern was repeated. Bishop Pedro De Landa burned all but four books of Mayan literature. The Romans also contributed to this wholesale destruction of knowledge. They attacked Druidic libraries. When Rome destroyed Carthage in 146 B.C., they burned the great Punic National Library of over half a million volumes. They destroyed the library in Pergamus, the Semitic Library at Jerusalem and the Jewish Essen Library (from which perhaps, the Dead Sea Scrolls were saved). Their most outrageous act was the destruction of the Library of Alexandria, the center of learning in the western World. During ancient times, libraries served the function

of universities. What they overlooked was destroyed soon enough by Moslem Arabs. Richard Wingate's brief list only highlights such activities, which are so innumerable as to be beyond recall. The end result has been the almost complete worldwide loss of ancient documents. If preserved, these documents would, without doubt, shed light on the First Civilization.

4. **The fragmentation of a formerly homogeneous human population.** Man recovered from the Atlantic catastrophe and the four reemerging civilizations were in place by 5,000 B.P. But these were quite independent of one another. As time went on, the fractionalization became even greater until by classical times an independent political entity rose in the form of the city-state. This erosion of the sense of oneness of man served to dampen the memory of the First Civilization. Wars, intolerant and irrational religions, and misplaced scholarship all took their toll in erasing its memory.

The end result of the above is that after man recovered from the catastrophe of 10,500 B.P. all continuity with the past, the First Civilization, was lost. But let us do our best with what we have and attempt to describe the First Civilization.

The First Civilization began in North Africa in what is now the Sahara desert. In the first part of the last Ice Age (117,000 to 40,000 B.P.) the Sahara was the perfect place for man to develop a civilization, the first ever. We recall that 150,000 years ago Homo sapiens were extant with physical size and brainpower superior to today's modern man. He was formidable in every way and could easily fit into today's modern society. (It would be totally improper to analogize early North African Homo sapiens with primitive peoples around the world encountered by Europeans in the 19th and 20th centuries. Most of these people have been evolutionarily stagnant for millennia, whereas North African Homo sapiens was a fast mover and was quickly civilized). We have arbitrarily set the date of 40,000 B.P. as the beginning of the First Civilization for a single reason. It is at this time that modern man began to move around the world, and this alone bespeaks the beginning of the First Civilization. At this time, he enters Europe by boat *from the west* and settles in the area of the two hundred art caves (which lie along rivers) where hunting, grazing, and very limited agricultural opportunities were available. But he did not arrive in large numbers until 15,000 to 10,500 B.P. because we note that this was when 80 percent of the artwork was done. As absolute proof of his civilized prowess, he settled the New World by boat and raft. What is the time frame for settling the New World? It is probably exactly the same as Europe's. In *Patterns in Prehistory*, Professor Wenke (p. 244–245) lists twenty sites in the New World with possible dates earlier than 13,000 B.P., but these need further verification. The oldest sites are in South America. By 12,000 B.P., the Clovis hunting point culture spread throughout South America and North America south of the ice sheet. If the immigration pattern to the New World followed that of Europe then there was a trickle of immigrants from 40,000 to 15,000 B.P., growing remarkably from the later time and continuing to 10,500 B.P. when the Americas were completely settled. Then the asteroid disaster struck. All immigration ended, and contact with the Old World was lost until A.D. 1492.

As the First Civilization produced this immigration around the world we make certain assumptions about its character. It was a worldwide maritime empire. It had ships, which sailed the Atlantic and returned. It had excellent maps—not to be equaled for 10,000 years. Its peak must have been at the height of immigration from North Africa to Europe and the Americas (15,000 to 10,500 B.P.). Ships capable of such voyages are timeless in design and can be either simple (the Vikings) or elaborate (some Medieval vessels). But it takes a high-cultural level to produce, maintain, and use such ships. Advanced technology is required to build a wooden ship. Provisions must be made and stored. Navigation must be calculated with a mind to the ship's mission—trade, transport, exploration, mapping, and a safe return. The weather must be taken into account along with ocean currents. In short, ships mean civilization. If that civilization is maritime, it is on the seashore. The First Civilization had another impulse toward locating on the seashore. The Sahara was rapidly drying up from 15,000 to 10,500 B.P.; people were leaving— gathering provisions, building rafts and boats. What was a good harbor 10,500 years ago may be discernible yet. Lixus, Cadiz, and the lost city of Tartessos are all possible First Civilization ports, but given the 400-foot seawater rise since 10,500 B.P., the ancient structures are probably gone, covered with sediment and seawater. In the New World a seaport will probably never be found for the following reasons: a) there probably never was one present; and b) it would be claimed by nature after 10,500

John Cogan

years of neglect. The bright side to this is the development of under-water archaeology. Anything underwater is over 10,500 years old. Stone structures may collapse from tsunamis and earthquakes, but the evidence is there, and as stated earlier in this book and in many other works, more proof is being found all the time. One more place to look as technology improves is the Azores Plateau. Its 154,000 square miles of land was above water during the Pleistocene with mountains in the north shielding the plain to the south. It basked in the warm waters of the Gulf Stream making this environment absolutely perfect for human habitation and maritime enterprise. Given a civilization that is extensively maritime, worldwide, and confined to the habitable part of the North African tropics, we can deduce other aspects of the development. It had to have a high degree of social organization, and this indubitably comes from a combination of rulers and priests. It was a theocratic state.

The immigration to Europe and the Americas was forced by the drying Sahara. It was not a welcome choice as such a journey could very well be a death sentence. But it was done because it had to be done. The First Civilization by 15,000 to 10,500 B.P. was suffering severely from overpopulation, exacerbated by the drying Sahara, and there was a mass exodus to Europe and the Americas.[57] Plato's story indicates there was also an exodus to the east at 10,500 B.P. that led to a war with the nation-states of Greece and Egypt. This last sentence contains an indirect observation of great importance. Ships provide an infinitely superior mode of transportation to overland journeys when immigration is involved. The same can be said for trade. Over a period of a few thousand years ships made it possible for the First Civilization to settle the New World from the southern tip of South America all the way to the southern rim of the North American ice sheet. Immigrants followed the rivers inland. Thus, two continents were quickly and easily settled—explaining the anomaly of why extreme South America has archaeological dates older than North America. This stands as a monstrous embarrassment to the savants who hold forth the "down through 3,000 miles of ice" theory of the population of the Americas. A land journey is more onerous than a sea journey in all respects. The dangers of the trail were both physical and from human attack. Other dangers were starvation, extremes in climate, backbreaking work, and the inability to prepare for the unknown. Problems transporting adequate supplies and safely navigating unknown territory plagued land journeys. Just think about how many camels or mules would be required to carry the cargo of one of the Egyptian burial ships found at the Great Pyramid for 1,500 miles. Even without computing, we know the answer is well in the hundreds and would take untold time. A ship sails twenty-four hours per day, and a camel or mule walks eight hours. Ships of the First Civilization settled the Americas efficiently, quickly, and safely.

We want to know what the First Civilization looked like on a day-to-day basis, and this is easy to answer. The Mesopotamian, Egyptian, and Central American civilizations at their prime *are* the First Civilization all over again—or at least its first cousins. They totally and utterly developed from the heritage of the First Civilization. This accounts for the remarkable similarities between them. Best of all, the Central American civilization was seen firsthand by European man, and the remaining ruins allow a mind's eye view of what life was like in Mayan times as well as during the First Civilization. As we noted in "Part III: The First Civilization," there are many similarities between the two mideastern civilizations and the Central American civilization. Almost invariably, these similarities can only be explained by heritage from the First Civilization, making our task of "reconstructing" the First Civilization much easier.

Architecturally, cities of the First Civilization must have looked much like Teotihuacán when it was Montezuma's capital and was first seen by Cortés. Step pyramids and great plazas dominated the scene with obvious careful attention paid to astronomical alignment (equinox, solstice) and geophysical alignment (true north). Artisans constructed foundations and walls using colossal stonework with ferrous oxide cement added to the blocks. There were provisions for freshwater and sewerage for waste. All the trappings of a city were there such as markets, ships, vendors, craftsman, artists, professionals, laborers, military, bureaucrats, and everywhere—priests. The city could hold a million people. Farther from the city, people like the Iceman of the Alps would lead their lives, using a combination of hunter gathering, agriculture, and herding.

The people of the First Civilization, whether in the Old World or the New World were remarkably homogeneous. They were of one race, red-skinned man. Schoolcraft concluded that the Indians of eastern America were representatives of a separate, independent, and unique race and were not derived from any other race (for example, Asian).[58]

Schoolcraft argues in *Archives of Aboriginal Knowledge*:

> The syntax and plan of thought of a people may remain, when the sounds of the language have almost totally changed. We find this true of nearly all our American tribes, in whom the order of thought constitutes a trait of coincidence almost as uniform as their physiology.
> (Henry Rowe Schoolcraft, *Archives of Aboriginal Knowledge*, p. vii)

The red American Indian of 1492 was the direct descendant of the people of the First Civilization. Henry Rowe Schoolcraft, the scholar that knew them best, found them mentally and physically alike. It is not surprising then that further study caused later scholars to determine that in the dim past (that is, the First Civilization) there was only one language. Even more surprising, the world's foremost expert on mythology, Joseph Campbell, finds a worldwide "universality of the basic thesis and motifs of mythology." Almost all paleohistorians agree that at an early time there was only one language and a worldwide common mythology. A common worldwide language and mythology serves as powerful evidence of the success of the First Civilization's transport system. Geographic isolation leads to a proliferation of language and mythology. In 1492, instead of one language, Columbus found 400 languages spoken in the New World, clear proof of the hardship of recovery from the catastrophe of 10,000 years before. This is also proof of the destruction of the homogeneousness of the First Civilization.

Our next question is why did all four of the reemerging civilizations fail? We will dismiss all of the obvious reasons such as war or being eclipsed by other stronger, more vibrant civilizations. Instead, we will focus on the relationship between the reemerging civilizations and the First Civilization from which they are cloned. Is there anything that they inherited that contributed to their demise? All four suddenly appeared, rose to a great height, and then declined. In Egypt's case the decline was spectacularly fast. Within 150 years of building the magnificent Great Pyramid subsequent structures were markedly inferior, until all such effort dwindled off and died. The loss was so total that later generations of Egyptians did not know who built the pyramids, how they were built, or what they were used for.

It appears that each of the reemerging civilizations reached a peak of development that equaled the First Civilization's. This exhausted their stores of knowledge and they were unable to continue forward, increase their knowledge, or grow and prosper. All four were theocratic states; this is a sure formula for eventual failure. Take note of how the Christian church plunged western Europe into a 1,000-year period of stagnation known as the Dark Ages. Secularism finally saved western man, but religion continues to plague and obstruct a great part of the world reducing these adherents to an inferior status and imperiling world peace. Worse, in the First Civilization all knowledge was invested in the priesthood, which jealously guarded and monopolized it. Knowledge was the major source of their power raising them above the mass of people. This status helped the priests equate themselves with ruler-administrators. All four reemerging civilizations aped this cultural fashion, and their attention to the real world waned as the priests pursued their esoteric and arcane works.[59] Vestiges of holding knowledge secret continued long after these civilizations fell. In Phoenician times (5,000 to 1,000 B.P.) trade routes were secret under pain of death. Ship construction technology was secret. By the time of Aristotle, Plato, and Socrates (400 B.C.) these worthies disdained practical science and manual work and were totally oblivious to the practical application of knowledge. Archimedes of Syracuse (287–121 B.C.), Galileo Galilei (A.D. 1564–1642) and Sir Isaac Newton (A.D. 1643–1727) would forever put to rest the idea of secrecy regarding practical matters. It took thousands of years to get advanced knowledge out of the hands of priests and into the mainstream of human effort where it could do some good. Other effects of priestly secrecy are obvious. Progress was slow and depended on disinterested priests. A savage war would wipe out the priestly caste and whatever records it might have and a whole civilization's scientific knowledge would be lost. In summary, the First Civilization passed on its stored knowledge in large part to the four reemerging civilizations, who utilized it as far as they could. Lacking the competence to continue increasing practical knowledge—primarily because of the priestly monopoly and its secrecy—they eventually collapsed. The collapse occurred because, after their peak, the four civilizations became retrograde due to stultifying religion, wars, overpopulation, poverty, and intellectual inertia. They only copied the First Civilization for a short time; they could not continue on their own. There is also a far more subtle cause of the failure of these civilizations. The Homo sapiens who survived the asteroid strike suffered physical and mental degeneration as a result of radiation poisoning and were by no means the equals of their forebears prior to 10,500 B.P.

The Maya civilization was an independent but large and significant part of the reemerging Mesoamerican civilization. Only a few centuries before Cortés, the Mayan civilization, a very accomplished high Stone Age civilization mysteriously failed—utterly and completely—leaving hundreds of abandoned pyramid complexes across the landscape. Modern scholars do not know but seek the cause of the collapse. In his excellent book *Maya* Charles Gallenkamp devotes Chapter 13, "Warfare Disunity and Decline: The Maya Dark Age," to exploring the mystery. Most of Mayan country was some of the worst real estate in the Americas, tropical jungle suitable for only slash and burn agriculture. Yet population soared as evidenced by many monumental structures, all of them with theatrical importance and illustrative of the power of the aristocracy and priesthood. These parasites owed their status to heredity and nothing else. Vast human sacrifice required war for captives to serve as victims. The end came quickly through intercity warfare, revolts, insurrections, defacing monuments, and the elimination of the aristocracy and priestly class. Within one hundred years some of the Maya made feeble efforts at reconstructing the old knowledge; however, it had been lost. "At Tikal these survivors were so culturally impoverished that they had sometimes reset monuments upside down or backwards, as if their hieroglyphic texts could no longer be read." (Charles Gallenkamp, *Maya,* p. 149)

Our next question is how many people died, and how many survived the asteroid strike? Unfortunately, we can only hazard a guess. Before we begin we know that we are dealing with millions of people. Only a population well into the millions could establish the First Civilization. "The Gap" or Mesolithic age lasted for 5,000 years before civilizations reemerged; the survivors of the catastrophe must have been few in number to require such a long recovery. By a very rough estimate recovery in the New World was such that by A.D. 1492 there were 42 million indigenous Americans. But we still have no way of knowing how many there were at 10,500 B.P. before and after the asteroid impact. We also do not know how many had crossed the Atlantic to the New World between 15,000 and 10,500 B.P. (or before).

The Troano Codex is one of the four pre-Spanish invasion manuscripts that survived destruction by Spanish priests and soldiers. It presently is in the Museum of Archaeology and History in Madrid. Codices are Mayan books with leather or wood covers. The paper is made from the bark of the wild fig tree, folded accordion-style, measuring 8 to 9 inches wide and several yards long. This document has been translated by Abbé Brasseur de Bourbourg. (Brasseur 1814–1875 (?) was a French cleric far more interested in archaeology than the Church.) The following excerpt provides more evidence for the New Order:

> In the sixth year of Can, on the eleventh Muluc of the month of Zar, terrible earthquakes occurred and lasted until the thirteenth Chuen. Mur, the land of the clay hills, and the land of Mound were its victims. They were rocked twice and suddenly disappeared in the night. The Earth's crust was continuously raised and lowered in several places by the subterranean forces until they could not longer withstand the pressure, and many countries were separated from each other by deep rifts. In the end, both countries sank in to the ocean with 64,000,000 inhabitants. It happened 8060 years ago.
> (Otto Muck, *The Secret of Atlantis*, p. 183)[60]

Old Order scholars scoff at this translation. Not because the translation is inaccurate—they cannot translate it at all. They object to the translator, Brasseur, whom they view as a deluded visionary because of their own views (that is, there never was such a catastrophe, there weren't that many people, and man was not even civilized 8,060 years ago). Brasseur was a consummate scholar who devoted his life to Mesoamerican studies. He used primary sources and lived with the people. It was Brasseur who discovered Bishop Landa's book, *Ralacion de las cosas de Yucatan*, in the Library of the Academy of History in Madrid in 1863. From this source he was able to discern the Mayan method of counting and decipher hieroglyphic writing leading to the discovery of the Mayan obsession with time and their calendar. He came to believe that the advanced Mesoamerican civilization had roots elsewhere. This led others to belittle his work. We should now take it seriously, however, because we have exhaustive independent evidence of the catastrophe, its date, and that it wiped out a prior civilization.

In the roster of early Mayan archaeologists, Brasseur was a pioneer of the first rank. If he did little to discover and describe the physical remains of Middle American cultures, he supplemented that approach brilliantly by exploring the documentary field. He opened up more avenues and preserved and utilized more records than any other Americanist of the nineteenth century.

(Robert L. Brunhouse, *In Search of the Maya*, p. 131.

It is estimated that there were 40 to 42 million indigenous Americans in A.D. 1492. The European invasion of the Americas reduced this number immediately and precipitously.[61] But can we use 42 million as a starting figure to extrapolate back to the number of survivors of the catastrophe of 10,500 B.P.? Unfortunately, the answer is "no." There is no accurate way to obtain vital statistical information required for the calculation (a small variance in the birth rate or death rate applied over the generations that lived between 10,500 B.P. and A.D. 1492 produces a difference of many millions of people). We can note however, that the American Indians in the tropics have been prolific, and in spite of the European decimation following A.D. 1492 they now number several hundred million. There is no doubt that the First Civilization numbered well into the millions of people.

The next question to consider is how did the asteroid impact physically affect man? After the catastrophe of the asteroid impact man was greatly reduced in numbers. This was particularly true in the tropical zone of Eurasia and Central America, which was his natural habitat. Undoubtedly, there were a few who survived somehow, but the majority of the survivors would be outside of the tropics. They were not safe, however. They would suffer the same radiation hazard as the megafauna of the earth. In retrospect it is obvious that the human survivors of the disaster, while not going extinct, did in fact suffer serious physical setbacks. They endured the degenerative effects of radiation poisoning—smaller stature, physical weakness, poorer sense of sight, smell and hearing, smaller brain size, increased propensity to cancer, and a shorter life span. The archaeological record is quite clear that man suffered this fate. The skeletons of Cro-Magnon man (40,000 to 10,500 B.P.) tell us that he was a superb physical and mental specimen, over six feet tall with a brain capacity larger than modern man's. After 10,500 B.P. man enters the Mesolithic age (10,500 to 5,000 B.P.), which all scholars recognize as a time of retrogression. Artifacts are rare and inferior to those from prior times. Archaeology and anthropology have very little to say about the Mesolithic age. The cause of this regressive phenomenon is an unexplained mystery to the Old Order. Just after this 5,000-year period of regression and lack of accomplishment in the tropics, the reemerging civilizations appear, created "suddenly," "spontaneously," by people "who came from somewhere else." This is clearly the coalescing of a few hardscrabble survivors from the areas of major destruction (the Northern Hemisphere and northern part of the Southern Hemisphere) and survivors from outside the disaster area. Both groups show the ravages of the radiation experience. Physically they are much smaller. In the Middle Ages the height of a full-grown man was 5 feet, 4 inches. Mentally, man seems to have suffered as well. His brain size is smaller, more proportionate to his diminished body. His senses are poorer; his instincts duller. All four reemerging civilizations fail. The cause seems to be that after aping the First Civilization they were incompetent to continue forward.

Given the rapid decline of all four civilizations, especially the Egyptian, it appears that knowledge slipped away instead of increasing. In fact, in the first one hundred years of each civilization that reemerged, we detect no scientific progress beyond the skills they had upon arrival. The decline permeated the whole social structure. An astute observer concludes that diminished physical and mental capacity due to radiation poisoning was a very significant factor in the failure. Only now 10,500 years later is man as physically and mentally able as he was when the asteroid struck.

Our next query explores the question, what factors combined caused "The Melt"? It took 117,000 years for the great ice sheets to reach maximum glaciation during the last Ice Age. Yet this immense amount of ice did not take an equal time to melt, as common sense says it should. Instead it melted precipitously and retreated to its present position in only 4,000 years (10,500 to 6,500 B.P.). Conventional thinking turns immediately to the Milankovitch cycles for an explanation but they obviously do not apply as they are too lengthy in duration (the earth's axial tilt varies from 22° to 24° every 41,000 years; the earth's axis of rotation wobbles and a full wobble takes 25,800 years; the earth's orbit around the Sun changes from circular to elliptical and back every 93,000 years). In fact, the Milankovitch cycles are absolute proof that the great ice sheets would require about 117,000 years to melt under normal circumstances. Only the asteroid impact can explain the rapid melt. But exactly how did it cause the melt? The Camp Century Greenland ice core tells us how the asteroid changed the earth's atmosphere. At the 10,500 B.P. mark it records four things: 1) massive volcanic ash fall; 2) massive increase in atmospheric carbon dioxide; 3) copious sea salts in the atmosphere; and, 4) an instantaneous rise in atmospheric and ocean water temperature. There is good evidence that the asteroid impact moved the earth's crust in the direction of its flight path, which would bring the North American ice sheet closer to the equator. It also simultaneously increased the tilt of the earth's axis of rotation, thereby allowing more solar heat to reach the Arctic. There is also strong evidence of the subsidence of the North Atlantic Ridge. Because of this, the Gulf Stream now reaches Europe. From the above data we discern four facts that raised the earth's temperature thereby causing the precipitous melt:

1.   The ash fall
2.   Increase in carbon dioxide
3.   Change in ocean currents
4.   Axial tilt, crustal movement

The ash fall from the asteroid impact covered all the ice in the Northern Hemisphere. In some places it was thick and in others thin. Only a thin coating is sufficient to cause glacial ice to melt. Dust from the Sahara blown onto glaciers in the Alps causes extremely rapid melting. The dark-yellow layer of dust absorbs solar radiation, and the white snowfields no longer reflect sunlight. Such a storm was responsible for melting the ice and uncovering the 5,500-year-old Iceman in the Alps in 1991.

The massive increase in carbon dioxide in the atmosphere had two sources. First, it was the major component of the gases contained in the volcanic magma; second, it came from deepest parts of the Atlantic where huge currents were created in the stagnant seawater carrying it to the submarine volcanic sites where it mixed with the volcanic explosions thereby releasing the dissolved carbon dioxide. Both sources (magma and seawater) were required to produce the massive amount of carbon dioxide that led to the melt.

The subsidence of the Mid-Atlantic Ridge allowed the Gulf Stream to flow unobstructed to Europe, a major factor in causing the quick melt of the European ice sheet; and the Gulf Stream continues to give Europe its mild weather. The rising North Pacific Ocean overflowed the

Bering Strait and warm water was admitted into the Artic Ocean causing the North American ice sheet to melt in all directions—greatly speeding up its melt.

Strong evidence exists that the asteroid impact caused some crustal movement toward the equator and some increased axial tilt. This would allow more solar heat to reach the northern latitudes and contribute to the rapid melt.

CHAPTER 25: THE NEW ORDER VERSUS THE OLD ORDER

The New Order of man's history holds three major points. There was a First Civilization. It was destroyed by an asteroid that hit the earth 10,500 years ago. Man recovered and formed four reemerging civilizations after 5000 B.P. The Old Order is based on two pillars: first, that civilization began in the Mideast 5,000 B.P.; second, Asians settled the Americas by crossing the Bering land bridge and then proceeded south. Both pillars of the Old Order are demonstrably false. The Achilles' heel of the Old Order is the second pillar. If the Americas were not settled in this fashion then there is no alternative but the New Order hypothesis: the Americas were settled by people who crossed the Atlantic in ships. Ships are only built by civilized people. There was a civilization in North Africa that provided both the ships and people. Archaeological dates show that the period of greatest immigration to the Americas (and to Europe) was 15,000 B.P. to 10,500 B.P. The Old Order refuses to admit that man was civilized at this time. According to the Old Order man was first civilized in the Mideast at 5,000 B.P. and was quite land bound. As has been painstakingly argued, this is actually man reemerging from the asteroid impact catastrophe. The Old Order has been decoyed into believing that this is the beginning of man's civilized era.

In "Part III: Chapter 15: Beringia Did Not Happen," the reasons that disprove the Beringia theory are given and need not be repeated here, but some further comment is in order. The theory itself is seventy years old and of obscure origin. It initially was met with much misgiving and disbelief. Because there was no alternative theory, it slowly infected academia to the point that today it is the only theory taught. "Taught" is even an inappropriate word. The theory is always set forth in a few sentences or barely a page in an otherwise comprehensive text. The reason for this is simple: the theory is pure speculation, devoid of any substantiating facts. Hence a few sentences are all that can be said about the theory. It cannot be described. It cannot be dated (the "arrival" dates are all backward for the theory as the earliest ones are in deep South America and the Beringa theory expounds that Asians entered the Americas from the north). It cannot explain the present lack of any modern Asians who are descendants of the original migrating people. It cannot explain the total lack of similarity to any Asian culture. It cannot explain the total lack of any relationship to any Asian language. Textbooks of the Old Order find it far more convenient to avoid these embarrassing questions. Therefore a page or two of text in the most general terms suffices to state the Beringia theory. Then these texts move on to other, more comfortable matters. If it were a valid theory it should be able to be tested through replication, just as Thor Heyerdahl replicated the building and sailing of a balsa raft and a reed boat. Unfortunately, for the Old Order, no anthropologist has the faintest idea how men, women, and children got through 3,000 miles of ice, a thousand miles of jungle, avoided fatal disease and starvation. Hence no academician can replicate the journey. It exists only in the imagination. And no academician seems eager to try it. There are no Thor Heyerdahls in academia! Yet the Old Order passes off this theory as science! The Beringia theory can only be expressed in generalities, cannot be articulated in detail, has no supporting factual evidence, and cannot be replicated! The theory is not science; it is purely a product of misguided speculation. It is an embarrassment to science.

Thus, the two pillars of the Old Order are false. The result is chaos. It is destroyed. However, the Old Order will never admit this. It will be replaced by the New Order in exactly the same fashion that other revolutionary ideas have been accepted in the past. The proponents of the Old Order will gradually disappear by retirement and death. New blood will enter paleohistory, and the New Order will be accepted.[62]

The Old Order will not be missed. It has serious marks against it. It has wasted fifty years time in the sciences of anthropology and paleohistory by chasing after the wrong scent. It is massively defensive about its two-pillar foundation. This has led to deplorable results. It actually fears rather than welcomes archaeological discoveries. An example of this is underwater archaeology. Anything found under the ocean's waters is 10,500 years old or more. This is impossible according to the tenets of the Old Order, which maintains that man was not civilized at that time. As a result academicians shun underwater archaeology. The last thing they want to find is something there. Amateurs (defined as those who do not get a government paycheck) have to do it all. The Old Order ignores pertinent paleohistorical facts that do not comport with its two pillars. For instance you will not find reference in Old Order textbooks to the legends of New World Indians, which state that these peoples came from the east (and that no legends refer to the north). "Ignoring" becomes deception when a number of pertinent facts are omitted from an academic text because they contradict the two precepts of the Old Order. For example, the Old Order never mentions Professor Hapgood's ancient maps; Indian legends that tell of coming from the east; reports that American Indian blood type was type O, not Asian's type A or B; and, the demographics of the New World in A.D. 1492: 30 million Native Americans in South America, 10 million in Central America and 2 million in North America—all of which disproved the twin canons of the Old Order. To omit such facts and yet present a text as complete is scientific deception.

The Old Order stands charged with ignorance. Thor Heyerdahl (who has been totally ignored by the Old Order) flatly accuses anthropologists of being abjectly ignorant of ships, the ocean, and ocean currents.[63] Barry Fell has translated many epigraphs, proving pre-Columbian contact between the Old and New Worlds (another subject that is anathema to the Old Order), and laughs at academicians who cannot comprehend that Indian rock art is a readable message, and that the language of many American Indian tribes contains words that are undeniably Egyptian, Phoenician, Welsh, or that there is ample proof of extensive pre-Columbian sea trade between American Indians and the peoples of the Pacific and Atlantic Oceans.

Anthropology is the study of man in his entirety. Archaeology, by contrast, is "the scientific study of the material remains of past human life and activities, such as fossil relics, artifacts, monuments, etc." Anthropology is associated with schoolroom science and archaeology with a "dig" at a prehistoric site. But modern anthropologists seem to have forgotten their job description. Myths, legends, and oral histories contain information of absolute value to paleohistorians. This information is left out of the best modern anthropological works. There are reasons for this. First, many anthropologists do not understand the ancients' ways of communicating information by myth and legend. Most are completely ignorant of the fact that Native Americans and others *have* oral histories; second, they arrogantly *assume* that the legends are fanciful, and therefore, a waste of time to a serious scholar; finally, the very fact the ancients wasted so much time memorizing, transmitting, and recording such fanciful stories shows how ignorant they were. It never occurs to these anthropologists, who are in the great majority, that it is *they* who are ignorant and cannot understand what they are being told. The best way to illustrate this scientific deficiency is to take the *best* anthropological reference work used in the preparation of this book as an example. The American Museum of Natural History has sponsored a work known as *The Illustrated History of Humankind.* Volume I is *The First Humans, Human Origins and History to 10,000 B.C.* Many outstanding authors contributed chapters to the book. Yet not once in the entire book is there a reference to the innumerable myths and legends of man's paleohistoric past. In fact the words legend or myth do not even appear in the Index. The book gives the usual perfunctory statement (less than one page out of 227 pages) that the New World was settled by Asians who came from Siberia, a statement only to be accepted, not to be explained. No mention whatsoever is made of the fact that numerous tribes of the New World have legends (thousands of years old and all remarkably alike) that they came from the east across the Atlantic Ocean. What is the purpose of the omission? Without this knowledge the Siberian theory is certainly strengthened, as the legends are a major contradiction to it. Equally embarrassing is the fact that there are no legends of a journey from the north. But *science* requires that a theory account for *all* the facts so the omission is scientifically unacceptable. Further, it shows contempt for the integrity of the Native Americans it studies. It is a definite statement that they are ignorant and do not know what they are talking about. They cannot possibly know where they came from; only the anthropologists know that, and it is from Siberia not from the east. *The First Humans* is one of the best paleohistory and paleoanthropological reference works, but it is guilty of an incomplete, unscientific, biased, and erroneous presentation.

The scorecard of the Old Order is not good. It is zero for three: 1) it missed the existence of an entire civilization; 2) it missed the asteroid strike; and 3) it has mistaken the four reemerging civilizations for man's original civilization.

With the above handicap it is not surprising why the Old Order cannot explain the following questions:

1. Who prepared Professor Hapgood's ancient maps?
2. How could the Egyptians and Mayans be so good at astronomy?
3. How did Homo sapiens populate the New World and why?
4. What caused the Melt?
5. What caused the great extinction of megafauna?
6. Why did "The Gap" (The Mesolithic Age) occur?
7. Why did four civilizations appear suddenly, spontaneously, in full flower created by people who came from somewhere else?
8. How can these civilizations have so many similarities?
9. How can there be so much evidence of an ancient worldwide language and mythology?

The New Order answers all these questions easily and convincingly—and proves they are interconnected!

The Old Order never will answer these questions until it accepts the three precepts of the New Order:

1. There was a First Civilization.

2. It was destroyed by an asteroid strike.

3. Man recovered, as the four reemerging civilizations attest.

After these three points are accepted, everything falls into place and these "mysteries" of paleohistory are easily solved. The future belongs to the New Order. All recent (1950 to present) anthropological research and archaeological finds support the New Order and disprove the Old Order; we can expect more of the same. In science there is one absolute, the theory must fit the facts; the facts must not be rigged to fit the theory. The Old Order violates this rule. Also, in science the best theory is one that is simple and explains the most facts. "When you have the truth everything fits." (From *Earth's Shifting Crust*, Hapgood, C.) By this standard, the New Order wins and the Old Order loses.

CHAPTER 26: THE FUTURE

With the New Order in charge, what should it do? It should fill in some of the archaeological holes created by the selective application of archaeological investigation by the Old Order. The most glaring of these has been past inattention to the legends of the New and Old World. These need to be recounted, cataloged, and reexamined in light of the tenets of the New Order (that is, the First Civilization, the Asteroid, and Man's Recovery). This includes myths of a fanciful nature which are significant like the legend of Phaethon falling from the sky as a result of flying too close to the Sun. This is an allegory for the fall of the asteroid; expressed in such fashion so as to aid memory as ancient man was want to do. The New Order sheds light on countless legends of the world (stories of the past, historical but not verifiable) especially those whose subject matter is how the New World was populated. "We came from the east," "across the ocean," "from a sunken land" all take on a new and significant meaning under the New Order. The story of the maelstrom and disaster of the human race told by the *Popol Vuh* is now quite understandable. That old standby, the legend of Atlantis, takes on quite a different light under the New Order. Entirely new considerations come to the fore such as desertification, forced emigration from the Sahara, boats to Europe and the Americas, a war between North African invaders and Greece and Egypt, the fall of the asteroid and a civilization rising 5,000 years "too soon" for conventional wisdom. This is heady material. American Indian oral history must be thoroughly examined. This will be especially difficult because of the proprietary rights of the Indian historians to the story, Indian cultural taboos and injunctions against its repetition to non-privileged persons and an Indian "copyright" against its repetition by non-Indian historians. Marvelous information lurks here. In northern British Columbia some Indian oral histories refer to the retreating ice and the rising oceans. It, therefore, goes back 7,000 to 10,000 years and is collaborative proof of the Ice Age, the melt, the populating of British Columbia from the south as the ice melted, no Asian migration from the north and who knows what else. It appears that the Old Order, to its shame, was absolutely unaware of the existence of Indian oral histories.[64]

The search for the locations of the First Civilization's major cities must continue, but with new knowledge that the sites were demolished by the asteroid impact, are likely to be 400 feet under salt water or buried under a modern city. Possibly better luck will be obtained in a search for the location of other settlements or cities of the survivors of the Atlantic catastrophe. Presumably these will be in the Southern Hemisphere south of the destruction zone. Monte Verde would be a case in point, as people there would have survived the disaster. However, we hope to find much larger settlements of the same date.

Above all, underwater archaeology must be well funded and actively pursued. It has received short shrift long enough. New technology must be used. Underwater exploration technology has vastly improved in the last decades as witnessed by the recovery of a Russian submarine from 17,000 feet deep in the Pacific Ocean by the Glomar Explorer in 1974 and the discovery of the *Titanic* in 1985 at a depth of 12,500 feet on the bottom of the Atlantic. The Azores Plateau is 10,000 feet deep (the legendary home of Atlantis); perhaps something could be seen there. The Russians claim they have but have not shared their pictures. Close to shore, within the area of the Holocene sea rise ancient ports of call might be found, but they will be under tons of ocean sediment and the technology required to penetrate these layers is very much in its infancy.

New technology may solve one of paleohistory's most important problems. Since the American Indians came to the New World from somewhere else (Old Order—Asia; New Order—North Africa) where are their ancestors, and who are their ancestors? This could be determined by identifying these ancestors' present descendants in the area of origin. The Old Order has tried extremely hard to find the ancestral homeland of Native Americans in Asia, utterly and completely without success. And obviously no present population of Asians is related to the American Indian of 1492. Indian blood type O and Asian blood types A and B being mutually exclusive says it all. Across the Atlantic the story is quite different. In northwest North Africa in the environs of the Atlas Mountains live the Berber people. These people have copper-colored skin, dark eyes and hair, occidental eyes and type O blood. Many experts have sensed a relationship with the American Indian. The ancient Basque people of the Pyrenees Mountains between France and Spain are believed to be related to the American Indian. Again, the physical characteristics are similar: copper-colored skin, dark eyes and hair, occidental eyes and type O blood. The Basques have a unique language that is not cognate with any of the Indo-European family of languages. It is thought to be a living relic of Ice Age speech. The Basques need much further scrutiny as long-lost "cousins" to the American Indian. Progress in DNA analysis and other methods will make this possible.

In the New Order there are no restraints placed on one's range of imagination relative to archaeological research. It is welcome. There is no cutoff date for the formation of civilization, that is, 5,000 years ago in the Mideast, nor is there the dogma of a trek (by unknown people and by unknown means) through Siberian permafrost, down through 3,000 miles of ice, then desert, then mountains, then jungle, to the tip of South America. Freethinking in all exploration of the past is the rule.

This leads us to some of the mysteries of that very misunderstood continent, South America. In 1492, it held 30 million Native Americans. They were quite spread out and had largely abandoned the original area of settlement, the Amazon Basin, due to the weather change after the Ice Age when increased rain turned the tropical savanna into a rainforest jungle. But it appears there are traces of this earliest occupancy still extant and unexplored. In *Atlantis: The Eighth Continent*, Charles Berlitz provides two pictures of eight pyramids (overgrown with vegetation) in the Amazon Basin—unexplored, but they appear to be real pyramids. Several authors have written of a system of unexplored tunnels in the Andes Mountains, constructed at an ancient but unknown time by an unknown people. The tunnels may contain priceless artifacts, perhaps of the First Civilization. Mysteries such as the above used to incite anthropologists and archaeologists to riot, but the deadening weight of the armchair archaeologists of the Old Order has produced a dysfunctional lethargy in the face of great archaeological possibilities.

One South American mystery deserves special mention. It is the case of Father Carlo Crespi, a priest, a missionary, an explorer, an educated anthropologist, and very kind old man who lives in Ecuador and has for many years collected artifacts from the local Indians who brought them to him and sold them to him for a pittance (which was all the good man had). These items came from deep caves and tunnels in the vicinity of the confluence of the Santiago and Morono Rivers deep in the Ecuadorian jungle. The story is well told in Richard Wingate's, *Lost Outpost of Atlantis*. Some 70,000 items in all remain (the collection was largely destroyed once) and their uniqueness, even bizarre design, coupled with their ancient age mark many of the items as having no provenance from any known civilization. Can they possibly be artifacts of the First Civilization that have survived? Many items are not for decoration but for an unknown use, such as bronze pipes, gold and aluminum "wallpaper" sheets, woven copper items that look like an automotive radiator; other items are more mundane such as helmets, crowns, sculptures, plaques, pieces of copper made as hard as steel by an unknown method, and musical instruments. The Indians bring them to Father Crespi and have described abandoned cities in the jungle, tunnels (photographs have been taken of some of the tunnels), and pyramids. Interesting? Fascinating? Exciting? Not to the Old Order. The collection is a threat to the two pillars of their dogma and also is well beyond their comprehension. The Crespi collection has been purposefully ignored by the Old Order—abandoned—and its present status is unknown, a crime against science, deliberate, and loathsome. The New Order says, "It won't happen again."

A South American archaeological site that requires the most rigorous scrutiny is Arica, Chile on the Peruvian border. (It is described in an excellent article in the October 1986 issue of *Discover* magazine, "Secrets of the Mummies" by Gary Smith. The site is ignored by the Old Order.) Arica is a sea level city with 140,000 inhabitants. It lies on the shore of the very salty upwelling cold water of the Pacific and the Atacacama desert—the earth's driest piece of land. The city inadvertently produces a most unusual product: hundreds of ancient mummies. Practically every construction site unearths them and sometimes in large numbers. Dogs carry the bones down the street. The residents complain of the smell, and tell their children not to touch them or they will get pimples. The unique quality of the atmosphere and the soil has served to preserve the mummies, the oldest of which has been carbon dated at 7,810 years old. This is 3,400 years older than the most ancient Egyptian mummy, and various finds have produced a continuous chronological line to the near present (perfect for many things, such as a historical record of the evolution of certain diseases). The mummies were prepared by an amazingly sophisticated method of embalming—some were made to be standing statues—and are dressed in dyed woven clothing, with braided and coiffured hair, by no means primitive people. Their anthropological importance is immediately apparent. These are people who lived in the middle of the Mesolithic age, "the Gap" (10,500 to 5000 B.P.), whose ancestors were people of the First Civilization who survived the asteroid strike, the great extinction, and whose descendants would be the originators of the Peruvian and Central American civilizations in the years to come. As of 1986, two stalwart scientists were studying the mummies, Marvin Allison, a United States physician and paleopathologist, and Guillermo Focacci, a Chilean archaeologist. The Chilean government has not supported the project, neither has the United States, but the National Geographic Society has contributed some funding. The mummies embarrass the Old Order, because people were not supposed to be civilized then and support is withheld. Proper investigation of the Arica mummies is a paramount concern for the future—and another example of why the Old Order must go. The New Order is not dogma. It is a working hypothesis and the purpose of this book has been to organize and proffer the facts that we presently have in its favor. Taken as a whole, the evidence is very convincing and as more facts are added—by research pointed in the right direction—we will obtain a better understanding of man's paleohistoric past.

Part I: The Ice Age

CHAPTER 1: The Beginning

1. It is thought the earth grew from cosmic dust to its present size in only 70 million years as a result of cosmic collisions (that is agglomeration) therefore the impact rate must have been one billion times what it is today. The earth received its primordial compounds of carbon from such impacts and when earthly conditions became favorable for life the required materials for life were there, brought by impact with space debris. The Apollo missions to the Moon in the 1970s brought back moon rocks that failed to support any prior theories as to how the Moon was formed. These missions produced a new theory: The nascent earth had a cosmic collision with a huge interstellar object over 4 billion years ago which ejected debris that coalesced into the Moon.

CHAPTER 2: The First Ice

2. This is the interpretation of the Piggott cores taken from the North Atlantic Ocean by Charles S. Piggott on the ship *Lord Kelvin* in the 1930s. The four pulses of ice are discernable in alternating layers of cold water and warm water Globigerina (a microscopic plankton). These four major thrusts of ice during the Quaternary period for convenience will be referred to as the Ice Ages and the last thrust, which directly involves Homo sapiens, will be referred to as the Ice Age. The Ice Age ended abruptly at 10,500 years ago and this figure will be used to measure the Holocene epoch—the present time—on the Geological timescale (The Quaternary period is divided into the Pleistocene: the Ice Ages of 2.49 million years; and the Holocene, the present time of 10,500 years to the present.) The last major thrust of the ice occurred between 117,000 years and 10,500 years ago.

3. The earth's axis is not perpendicular to the plane of its orbit around the Sun. It tilts 22° to 24° over a 41,000-year cycle. The greater the tilt the colder the middle latitudes. Given the axial tilt, the earth has another movement, called the "wobble," whereby the axis itself describes a circle every 25,800 years. When the wobble adds to the tilt it is even colder. The earth itself goes around the Sun every year. Its orbit changes

from a near circle to an ellipse and back in a cycle of approximately 93,000 years. The more elliptical the orbit, the colder the earth.

CHAPTER 4: Aridity
4. It is estimated that the average interglacial period between pulses is 10 to 15,000 years.

CHAPTER 6: The Ice Today
5. In the northern desert, winter temperatures can be below freezing. The Sahara is not on the equator. It is mid-latitude and superimposed on North America would reach from Central America to the middle of the United States. Its location on the globe is referred to as in the dry tropical latitudes.

Part II: Man out of Africa
CHAPTER 7: The CT Boundary
6. The geologic timescale is determined primarily by the age of stratified rock, which has become known through the work of geologists for several centuries. Although quite accurate, it is nevertheless an estimate, and less accurate the further back in time.

CHAPTER 8: Man Appears
7. This of course led to many amusing episodes. Two are worthy of note that involve Professor of Biology Thomas H. Huxley who championed Darwin's views throughout England (Darwin was very reclusive at this time of his life) and for his efforts became known as "Darwin's Bulldog."

One day Huxley was walking on a street in downtown London when from the other direction came a great lord from the House of Lords who approached Huxley and said, "I say Huxley, do you suppose Darwin can be right?" Huxley replied, "Of course." Long silence. Then the lord said, "But couldn't he have kept it to himself?"

A well-known anecdote is that of the encounter between Huxley and the unctuous Bishop Samuel Wilberforce of Oxford University (called "Soapy Sam" by his admirers because of his love of the sound of his own highly cultured voice). The occasion was a debate, or discussion, about evolution. Wilberforce spoke first, droning on and incidentally proving that he knew absolutely nothing about evolution and had probably never read *Origin of Species*. However, the attending audience of highly bred people was much prejudiced in his favor. At the end of his speech in an attempt at levity, he condescendingly looked at Huxley and asked "I beg to ask you, Professor Huxley, is it on your grandfather's or your grandmother's side you are descended from a monkey?" Immensely pleased with himself Wilberforce sat down to an outburst of applause. Huxley rose and addressed the audience and by forceful argument destroyed Wilberforce's presentation. At the same time Huxley made it clear that Wilberforce knew absolutely nothing about evolution and it was arrogant for him even to be talking about it. He concluded by directly addressing Wilberforce, "I assert that a man has no reason to be ashamed of having an ape for a grandfather. If there were an ancestor whom I should feel shame in recalling, it would rather be a man endowed with great ability and a splendid position who used those gifts to obscure the truth." An explosion of approval followed. An elegant lady gasped and fainted. Various clergy demanded to be heard and were refused by Chairman John Henslow who ruled that only scientific evidence would be discussed, religious miracles were excluded.

American buffoonery about evolution is captured in the Scopes Trial, the subject of various books and one movie. In 1925, the Tennessee legislature passed a law making it unlawful to teach any doctrine that denied the divine creation of man related in the Bible. High school teacher John T. Scopes taught evolution to his students and was tried, convicted and fined $100. The trial judge limited the trial to a single issue: had Scopes taught evolution? He admitted he had so that was the end of the matter—Hollywood notwithstanding. The constitutionality of the law and the validly of Darwin's theory of evolution and accuracy of the Bible were issues not reached by the court. That was too bad, as with William Jennings Bryan for the prosecution and Clarence Darrow for the defense, the trial promised excitement. Nevertheless, the trial obtained worldwide notice, and still serves as a monumental embarrassment as to the quality of intelligence extant in the United States. The Tennessee law was not repealed until 1967.

It is too bad that Darwin's father did not live to see how famous and respected his son became. While Darwin was at college (rejecting medicine and failing at theology as professions) his father wrote him: "You care for nothing but shooting, dogs, and rat-catching, and will be a disgrace to yourself and all your family."

8. For convenience this small chart gives an approximate anthropological timetable. All figures B.P. (before present).

Group	Time	Example
Hominoids	20m–present	Proconsul 18m
		Afropithecus 18m
		Lucy 3m
Australopithecines	3m–1m	
Homo erectus	2m–150k	Neanderthal 200k-20k
Homo sapiens	150k–present	Cro-Magnon 40k–present

Homo sapiens diverged from Gibbon and Orangutans 12–10m, from Gorilla and Chimpanzee 7–5m.

9. Procounsul is the name given to a fossil find made on Rusinga Island, Lake Victoria, (East Africa) in 1933 by Dr. L. S. B. Leakey and his wife Mrs. Mary Leakey.

10. Accepting the fact that man is an animal pursuing evolutionary development should not be so hard. It is well to contemplate the last sentence of Darwin's *Descent Of Man*, (p. 920):

We must, however, acknowledge, as it seems to me, that man with all his noble qualities, with sympathy which feels for the most debased, with benevolence which extends not only to other men but to the humblest living creature, with his god-like intellect which has penetrated into the movements and constitution of the solar system—with all these exalted powers—Man still bears in his bodily frame the indelible stamp of his lowly origin.

CHAPTER 9: Early Man

11. Man retained this trait through his 2 million years of hunter-gathering existence. Modern man (being enlightened?) rejects this practice and now only practices symbolic cannibalism as in Roman Catholic communion wherein by a miracle performed by a priest right in front of your eyes bread is turned into flesh and wine into blood of Jesus and it is eaten and drank by the participants. (A practice that George Washington called "a loathsome superstition.") It is to be noted that the ritual cannibalism of archaic man and today's man is for the same purpose: to

obtain the traits of the person being eaten.

CHAPTER 10: Modern Man

12. This is a good time to pose a question: is it reasonable to assume that a human being with this physical and mental ability will remain static in a hunter-gatherer lifestyle for over 145 thousand years and only begin civilization in the Mideast around 5000 B.P. as academia holds? No, this defies common sense and it did not happen at all, as we will see. Homo sapiens began civilization in North Africa more than 40,000 years ago. What the academics regard as the "beginning" of civilization is in fact the reemergence of man's civilization after the disaster of an asteroid impact on earth. Early Homo sapiens, a splendid animal superior to modern man, physically and mentally, did not waste 100,000 years as a hunter-gatherer with no progress toward civilization. In fact, he created a high Stone Age civilization, which was destroyed by the asteroid impact at 10,500 B.P. The academics have simply missed this historical fact. Further, we must remember that man can progress very fast. From the first day of the ancient Egyptian civilization to a man on the Moon took only 5,000 years.

CHAPTER 12: Accomplishments of the First Civilization

13. Exactly who and when Antarctica was discovered is an open question. Accordingly to legend a New Zealand Polynesian war canoe under command of Vi-te-Rangiora sailed as far south as the pack ice in A.D. 650. In A.D. 1820 three people claim its discovery by sighting land: a Russian expedition leader von Bellingshausen; an Englishman Bransfield; and an American Palmer.

14. One should pause a moment here and reflect upon the ease of an ocean crossing to the New World as opposed to a journey north through Siberia, across the Arctic, and down through 3,000 miles of ice.

15. The story of the discovery of the first Art Caves is a scientific thriller. A Spanish nobleman, Don Marcelino de Sautuola, owned an estate in the north of Spain near the city of Santander on the Bay of Biscay. In 1869, some of his neighbors were hunting foxes on his estate when one of the dogs fell into a hole in the middle of a field. The dog could be heard whining below and was rescued by the men after considerable effort. The hole was found to be in fact a cave and so Don

Marcelino was informed. He investigated the cave, was not impressed, and closed it up. Nine years later in 1878, Don Marcelino visited Paris and at the Paris International Exhibition of 1878 saw Ice Age tools and portable art that had been found in caves. In 1879, Don Marcelino and his daughter Maria returned to the cave (later to be called Altamira) to dig the cave floor and look for prehistoric artifacts. Little Maria, while playing looked up at the ceiling and saw "oxen"! Her father saw them almost unbelieving, and in short time guessed exactly that it was prehistoric art (in fact 15,000 years old). Don Marcelino wrote the luminaries of prehistory and anthropology at the time to tell of his discovery. He was ignored. In 1889, a meeting of these worthies was held at Lisbon for the purpose of discussing the Altamira art and then visiting the cave. The attendees were predisposed to believe prehistoric man was incapable of such magnificent art and upon a scurrilous charge of forgery by a local artist, the group decided that the art was a forgery, and therefore it was not necessary to visit the cave. They went home. Only years later when many more art caves were found in France and Spain was the authenticity admitted of all the art including that at Atlamira. Fittingly Altamira is the best example of the genre. The leading detractor of the authenticity of the Altamira art, one Emile Cortailhac, made a public and abject apology to Don Marcelino and Maria. It was too late for Don Marcelino who died of a broken heart after being vilified as a fraud, but Maria graciously accepted, and rewarded the born-again Cortailhac by telling him of other art caves not publicly known.

16. *Primitive Hearths in the Pyrenees* by Ruth Otis Sawtell and Ida Treat, is a charming book about the art caves. These two well-educated and adventuresome young ladies visited the Pyrenees Mountains in the summer of 1925 to do some archaeological-anthropological research on their own. They dug in a cave near the Trois Fre'res and found a 10,000-year-old skeleton, a wonderful find. They failed to keep the find a secret and faced a crisis when the local mayor, padre, and others wanted to give it a Christian burial. They went to visit a somewhat famous art cave and were told to go to a certain café in town where they would find the farmer owner having cheese and wine. They did, obtained a key to the gate (for a little money) visited the art cave and returned the key.

In his excellent book, *In Search of Adam,* Herbert Wendt tells a story so amusing it needs to be retold here. After World War II, the mayor of the town of Cabrerets, France one Monsieur Bessac rented the cave of Pech-Merle from the owner and converted it into a sort of subdued bistro complete with a bar (backed with a fabulous Ice Age woolly mammoth painting), electric lights, record player, postcards, cover charge, and the like. In 1952, the scent of dubiousness still lingered a bit over the art caves. Enter one Monsieur Breton, a rather self-important author who approached the mammoth, rubbed his thumb on its trunk and then laughingly showed Bessac his paint encrusted thumb, pointed at the smeared mammoth and said, "forgery, monsieur!" Bessac, enraged, hit Breton's hand a hard blow, threw him out of the cave, and sued him for a million francs. The defense of forgery failed and (somehow) the judge found the smudge damage to be twenty thousand francs.

17. This is reminiscent of the prehistoric art caves, just discussed, which display paintings of many animals extinct since 10,500 B.P., but which had for a long time coexisted with Homo sapiens.

18. Russian explorers claim to have found underwater monumental structures on the Horseshoe Archipelago (300 miles west of Gibraltar), and the Ampere Seamount. At present these finds have not been verified.

CHAPTER 13: The Sahara Dries Up

19. Even today the Sahara contains easily accessible artifacts that prove the existence of great numbers of people in the distant past that lived in even the most remote parts of North Africa. Author Jeremy Swift puts if beautifully:

> This knowledge that a secret life is going on (that is plant and animal life that does not appear during the day's heat, or until after a rain—even if that takes years) creates a feeling of mystery about the Sahara, which is deepened by the fact that everywhere in this desert are signs of intense human activity far in the past. There are large conical tombs made of piled rocks, and drawings and paintings on rock surfaces, showing herds of piebald cattle and ritual scenes whose participants wear strange headdresses and body decoration. In some area stone-age axes, arrowheads and fish harpoons lie so thick on the ground that you can walk about and pick up half a dozen in a few minutes. There are fossilized fish bones in the middle of arid wastes where it now rains once in ten years. At

times the desert looks like an inhabited landscape suddenly abandoned one afternoon thousands of years ago.

(*The Sahara*, p. 23)

See also, *Meeting Prehistoric Man*, G. H. R. von Koenigswald, (p. 175).

CHAPTER 14: The New World Is Settled

20. By a rough, but fair comparison, we can say that during this immigration from North Africa to Europe, 20 percent of the immigrants arrived between 40,000 B.P. and 15,000 B.P. Eighty percent of the immigrants arrived between 15,000 B.P. and 10,500 B.P. This same pattern exactly applies to the New World.

21. The people of North Africa with whom they traded knew the hard life in Ice Age Europe. Undoubtedly this influenced many emigrants to try their luck in the tropical, but far New World.

22. Christopher Columbus was successful on his voyage of 1492 because he rediscovered the long-lost secret of this circular pattern of the North Atlantic currents. He had traveled to Ireland and England and noted the wind was from the west, and he had traveled to the south and noted the Canary Current going to the west. Thus on leaving Spain he went south and caught the Canary Current to America. His three small caravels arrived there thirty-six days later. Once there, he knew that he had to go north to find the wind from west to east that would return him to Europe. Good fortune provided him with the Gulf Stream, which took him north. It is hard to believe that man lost the knowledge of this route for 10,000 years—from 10,500 B.P. to A.D. 1492. But this is true as after the asteroid impact there was no further immigration to the Americas until after A.D. 1492.

23. Today the crossing has become an annual small boat regatta. For example, the October 1998 issue of *Yachting World* contains a twenty-eight-page supplement, "How to Cross the Atlantic and All About the ARC." (ARC is Atlantic Crossing for Cruisers). This is an annual event where small boats cross 2,700 miles of ocean from Las Palmas (Canary Islands) to St. Lucia (former British Colony, Caribbean Sea, lesser Antilles, Windward Islands). From 1986 to 1997, 1,600 boats have made the trip as part of the rally. Many others prefer to go by themselves.

24. Ironically the Amazon rainforest is now threatened with extinction by man's fire. Overpopulation by man has sent subsistence living people into the jungle, who clear the forest with fire—slash and burn agriculture—so that they can plant their crops. These fires have gotten out of control, because in the dry season the Amazon rainforest can be tinder dry. Already hundreds of thousands of acres have been burned, and of course, thousands of acres logged.

25. There are many candidates for archaeological proof of man's earlier arrival in the Americas. Probably some of these will be verified in the near future. The Meadowcroft Rock Shelter in Pennsylvania tentatively dates to 17,000 B.P. and newly discovered Cactus Hill in Virginia tentatively dates to 18,000 to 16,000 B.P. South American offers (again tentatively dated) Pikimachay, Peru (25,000 to 15,000 B.P.); Pedra Furada (35,000 B.P.); Monte Verde (13,000 B.P. is accepted, 33,000 B.P. is speculated). For more comprehensive information on older sites in the Americas see, Robert J. Wenke, *Patterns in Prehistory* p. 236.

CHAPTER 15: Beringia Did Not Happen

26. Estimates vary from 20 to over 40 million with the higher number favored. Forty-two million is used for convenience. As the horror of Spanish Christian behavior sinks in, the realization develops that the number could actually be much larger. (Some authorities estimate 60 million.)

27. In an interview with the *Mammoth Trumpet*, Oregon State University, Vol. 9, No.1, 1993, archaeologist and Professor Alan Bryan gives a bit of personal history. In 1964, he moved to Alberta, Canada in order to be "at the heart of the hypothetical corridor" but determined that there were no Clovis points in the "corridor." In 1969, he left and adventured in Central and South America finding plenty of Clovis points. There are no Clovis points in the "corridor" itself and there are none in Alaska at its start. Nor have any ever been found in Siberia. However, the Clovis culture (12,000 to 10,500 B.P.) is endemic to the Americas and for it to be missing in the hypothetical corridor, Alaska, and Siberia, clearly indicates no Asian migration to the Americas occurred. However, the Clovis points found all over the New World are identical to those found in the art cave area of France and Spain. The Siberian lithic culture of the entire Pleis-

tocene bears no resemblance whatsoever to Clovis or any American lithic culture. Nor to any European culture.

28. This is not a small point. The harsh conditions of Siberia, the Arctic, and the great ice sheets make survival impossible without the use of strong, tough, adapted dogs. Native Americans totally lacked this kind of dog. In fact, the dogs found in the Americas most strongly resemble dogs of the Mideast.

29. Siberia is a subject worthy of a book itself. It comprises all of northern Asia and is about 4 million square miles in size. Much of it is technically a desert receiving 10 inches or less precipitation a year. It is extremely cold (many readings of –50°F)—very much colder than interior North America. Winter nights are long. Summer is very short. When it thaws in the arctic and subarctic the mosquitoes form clouds, the land becomes mud and it is impossible to travel. It is not a desirable place for man to live and has always had a very sparse population all during the Ice Age to the present time. The earliest inhabitants are thought to be a few tribes who fled into the area to escape warlike neighbors. Prior to contact with Europeans there was no agriculture; the people were and remain very sparse in numbers, physically small, extremely primitive, and loosely organized. In 1970, the indigenous population of Siberia was 151,000. There are probably no more than 30,000 in all the Siberian tundra. (Compare these numbers to 42 million Native Americans in 1492!) These primitive people are not descendents of the ancestors of the American Indian. They are different physically and have no advanced culture. This means that if Beringia was the route to the New World the pilgrims had to come from *beyond* Siberia. This adds another 3,000 miles to the trek and another anomaly: How did they get through Siberia without leaving a trace of their passage? And a corollary question: If we start the trek to the Americas on the far side of Siberia, how long does it take to reach Tierra del Fuego?

30. A comparable environment exists at present in the United States at Mount Washington in central New Hampshire. The mountain is 6,288 feet high, and in winter the wind is often over 100 miles per hour (one gust in 1934 was 231 miles per hour). When there isn't a blizzard the temperature often drops to –30°F and a pea-soup fog forms which requires

guide ropes for men to walk between adjacent buildings (one could be lost by taking only several steps out a door and into the fog).

31. There are many tales of adventurers versus the elements such as Scott and Shakleton in Antarctica; Peter Frenchen in the Arctic; the Donner Party in the Sierra Nevada of California; Balboa across the isthmus of Panama; but none of these could match the saga of the Asians descending through 3,000 miles of ice to populate the New World—bringing their wives and children and living off the land (ice?)—perhaps the Old Order cannot even fictionalize the account of the epic trek they so assiduously maintain occurred. (After his epic Antarctic trek in 1911-1912, Robert Falcon Scott and two companions died in their tent from the cold, trapped by a raging Antarctic blizzard only 11 miles from their home base and safety. A horrible testament to the savage weather on the ice.)

32. Modern vegetation in the hypothetical corridor is exactly the same as the vegetation everywhere else that was under the ice. And no fossil vegetation exists to prove otherwise. Thus, there is no physical evidence the ice-free corridor ever existed.

Part IV: The Asteroid
CHAPTER 16: Space
33. Unfortunately, the article is bare of any specifies as to the extinction, only postulating that the earth was darkened and: "A temporary absence of sunlight would effectively shut off photosynthesis and thus attack food chains at their origins . . . the large herbivorous and carnivorous animals that were directly or indirectly dependent on this vegetation would become extinct." But "many smaller terrestrial vertebrates did survive, including the ancestral mammals and they may have even been able to do this by feeding on insects and decaying vegetation." The paucity of information as to the physical consequences to earth of such an impact will become apparent when we fully discuss Dr. Muck's book, *The Secret of Atlantis*.

34. One entrepreneur has seriously proposed capturing an asteroid for the purpose of mining it! Geological theory is that much of earth's valuable minerals are leached out of its crust and are in the molten core, whereas asteroids have not suffered melting.

CHAPTER 17: The Asteroid Impact

35. This is the message of a book written by a great German scientist Otto Muck, *The Secret of Atlantis* (1978). Muck (pronounced Mook) was highly educated (a Ph.D. in Engineering from Munich College of Advanced Technology in 1921) and a scientific great (inventing the snorkel for German submarines in World War II and posted thereafter to the Peenemunde rocket team). After the war he was a consultant to industry and died in 1965 at which time he was said to own 2,000 patents. Muck's lifelong interest was ancient history and his convincing proof of the 10,500 B.P. asteroid strike allows us to make sense out of known geophysical facts and historical facts that are otherwise incomprehensible. (We will examine this point later, especially in "Part V: Man Recovers.") This section: "Part IV: The Asteroid," is most respectfully dedicated to Otto Muck.

36. This geophysical information did not come early or easily to man however, due to ignorance and religion. The early Greeks came very close to an accurate concept of the solar system. Heraclides (388–315 B.C.) thought the universe to be infinite, the spherical earth to rotate, and the planets to be separate worlds. Aristarchus of Samos (312–230 B.C.) proposed a heliocentric system. Eratosthenes (276–194 B.C) accurately measured the earth's circumference by an ingenious but simple method. On June 21, the longest day of the year, he observed the angle of the shadow of a well in Syene, Egypt at noon. A pillar in Alexandria, Egypt 500 miles north cast a shadow 7° more toward the north. If 7° equals 500 miles, then 360° equals 25,000 miles (rounded) for the circumference of the earth. But the Greek effort at astronomical accuracy failed. The culprit in all this was Aristotle (384–322 B.C.) who visualized the earth as a larger sphere (twice as large) which was the center of the universe; the universe being composed of a series of spheres one for each of the then known planets. These unfortunate mistakes, and others by Aristotle, became the dogma of the Christian church all through the Middle Ages. Copernicus, (A.D. 1473–1543) recognized the earth as merely a planet orbiting the Sun, like the others. His published work (A.D. 1543) was a book of tables rather than prose and it took the church twenty years to figure out that Copernicus said the earth went around the Sun. Fortunately, Copernicus had died by this time so was spared burning at the stake. Galileo (A.D. 1564–1642) was not so lucky. He professed the

Copernican view and in A.D. 1633 was tried before the Inquisition and found guilty of believing false doctrines "contrary to the Holy Scriptures" to wit; "that the Sun is the center of the world (universe), and that it does not move from east to west, and that the earth does move and is not the center of the world." For this crime he spent the last nine years of his life under house arrest (instead of prison by favor of the pope). With the birth of Sir Isaac Newton (A.D. 1642–1727), the West began to get back on track but the Christian fervor to destroy any "pagan" wisdom continued into the New World, where the incredible astronomical records of Mayans, Mexicans, and Peruvians, which were far superior to anything in the West, would be utterly destroyed by the religious fanatics of Spain.

37. This accounts for 95 percent of the world's active volcanoes. The Smithsonian Institute lists 1,343 potentially active volcanoes worldwide.

38. A 1964 marine earthquake off the city of Seward, Alaska caused a tsunami which on crashing ashore rolled a diesel locomotive for three blocks up a slight hill—and this was a small tsunami. Rachel Carson, author of *The Sea Around Us*, relates that storm waves from the North Atlantic Ocean have force of up to 6,000 pounds per square foot. At Wick, Scotland a violent storm in 1877 carried away a concrete pier-breakwater (secured with iron rods to the rock beneath) that weighed 2,600 tons. No ancient monumental structure could withstand a force like this. It would explode such a building.

39. Ships are little affected by tsunamis and simply ride over the great swell as it goes beneath them.

40. The sound of the Krakatoa volcanic explosion in 1883 went around the world several times.

CHAPTER 18: The Healing Earth

41. The loess deposits help us to appreciate the magnitude of the Atlantic catastrophe in another way: we can estimate the initial temperature of the death cloud. After the Mount Pelee explosion, it was found that the pyroclastic flow had in the neighboring town of St. Pierre melted glass (1,292°F), but not copper (1,981°F). The loess belt is rich in quicklime because of heat applied to the Atlantic seafloor material con-

taining seashells and other carboniferous materials which when heated to 1,600°F separates calcium carbonate and yields lime of commercial quality. Thus, the temperature of the death cloud was initially 1,600°F to 1,981°F.

CHAPTER 19: The Great Extinction

42. Taiga is a Russian word for the great forest belt just south of the arctic tundra, said to be the largest forest in the world. It is characterized by pines, spruces, larches (tamarack) all of which are conifer varieties. Deciduous trees such as birches, willows, poplars, and alders are found only along rivers.

43. These islands and their surrounding land were above sea level 10,500 B.P.

44. The most famous statement proposing the theory is a magazine article that reports finding iridium in rocks at the CT boundary. Iridium is uncommon on earth but common in asteroids. There is also a difference in soil found at the CT boundary (suggesting atmospheric dust). Many pages are wasted to "prove" that the asteroid was 10km (6¼ miles) in diameter, never suggesting the Adonis group. No reference to Muck is made. The magazine summary of the article says:

> Impact of a large earth crossing asteroid would inject about 60 times the objects mass into the atmosphere as pulverized rock; a fraction of this dust would stay in the stratosphere for several years and be distributed worldwide. The resulting darkness would suppress photosynthesis, and the expected biological consequences match quite closely the extinctions observed in the paleontogical record.

So the greatest threat is darkness for several years, plants don't grow, all dinosaurs die. Mammals survive, however.

> Many smaller terrestrial vertebrates did survive, including the ancestral mammals, and they may have been able to do this by feeding on insects and decaying vegetation.

L. Alvarez, W. Alvarez, F. Asara, H. Michel, "Extraterrestrial Cause for the Cretaceous–Tertiary Extinction," *Science,* Vol. 208, 6 June 1980: p. 1095.

Anyone who has read this book thus far and hopefully Otto Muck's book can only dismiss the Alvarez presentation as utterly inadequate.

Part V: Man Recovers
CHAPTER 20: Civilizations Suddenly Appear

45. Think of the significance of the casual phrase "man who is moving back into the devastated areas." This is weighty proof of the asteroid catastrophe. The Tigris-Euphrates and Nile Valley were the most verdant and desirable places to live in Eurasia, so why were they vacant? Only a catastrophe could account for this.

46. Thor Heyerdahl believes that the Sumerians, who say they came from "Dilmun" but whose location is unknown today, came from the island of Bahrain in the Arabian Gulf which was ancient Dilmun.

47. In fact, within 150 years of building the Great Pyramid subsequent efforts at pyramid construction were so inferior in quality that today all are damaged and some are only "mounds of sand and rubble." The *great* Pyramid Age was from 2686 to 2170 B.C.; that is, at the *start* of pyramid building, after this there was only decline.

CHAPTER 21: Cultural Evidence of the First Civilization

48. By A.D. 1500 the Chinese had the largest ships afloat. There were fleets of four-masted junks that carried 1,000 men each (a modern aircraft carrier has 4,000) and sailed the Indian Ocean exacting tribute under the Grand Eunuch Jeng Ho. By 1492 the West Coast of Mexico was a Chinese trade route. Visitors to the small Pre-Columbian Artifact Museum in Zihuatanejo, Mexico can see a huge painting depicting a seashore scene wherein a Chinese trader is showing a chest of clothing to several natives and a disapproving conquistador. Tourists at this small town visit and swim at Playa la Ropa—"clothing" beach which got its name from a Chinese trading vessel that sank nearby and the cargo of trade clothing drifted ashore at this beach—all before Columbus.

49. The Giza Pyramids recall Winston Churchill's remark about Russia "(they) are a riddle wrapped in a mystery inside an enigma." In *Fingerprints of the Gods*, author Graham Hancock recounts the theory of Robert Bauval that the three major pyramids establish a ground plan that is an exact replication of the Belt of Orion at 12,450 B.P. This was a unique date because only then did the meridional course of the Nile Valley exactly duplicate that of the Milky Way and the three stars of the Belt were at their lowest point in the sky of 11°08' at Giza. (The Belt cyclically rises to 58°11' and falls to 11°08' every 13,000 years because of the earth's axial precession.) Also at this date the Sphinx, with the body of a lion, would be looking squarely ahead at the rising of the constellation Leo (the lion) which would not happen again for 26,000 years upon a complete axial precession of the earth and the passing of the Sphinx nose by the twelve constellations of the Zodiac. Bauval's theory is to be found in his book, *The Orion Mystery*. It is well taken that the three great pyramids of Giza were built circa 2450 B.C. (8,000 years later than the Orion Belt alignment date), but the site plan would be perfectly preserved from knowledge which is a heritage from the First Civilization. The Sphinx is another matter. It probably was built at 12,450 B.P. or before, as it has ample evidence of suffering water erosion. The Sahara was acutely dry from 18,000 B.P. to 10,500 B.P. After the asteroid strike there was a brief respite with rain falling in modest amounts from 9,000 B.P. to 6,000 B.P. (during "The Melt") and thereafter almost total aridity. It would not seem to be enough rain to weather the Sphinx which being in a hollow has been buried in sand most of its existence. Another possibility is that the erosion was not produced by rainfall over a long period of time (as this did not happen) but rather was caused by the massive rainfall from the aftermath of the asteroid strike.

50. For instance only the New World has produced Mickey Mouse. It would be unusual beyond all mathematical chance for Mesopotamia to produce an identical Mickey Mouse. If it does there is some practical explanation, and in anthropology if there is no contact between Mesopotamia and the New World then the explanation is heritage from the First Civilization, which must have had a Mickey Mouse.

51. For lists of Mideast and Mesoamerica commonalities the reader is referred to:

Thor Heyerdahl, *Early Man and the Ocean*, p. 84–91, 73–75, 95

Ignatius Donnelly, *Atlantis: The Antediluvian World*, p. 136–165

Thor Heyerdahl, *The Ra Expeditions*, p. 25, 112, 117, 259–265, 287, 291

Lewis Spence, *The History of Atlantis*, p. 219–234

Peter Tompkins, *Mysteries of the Mexican Pyramids*, p. 350–351

J. Rowe, "Diffusionism and Archaeology," *American Antiquity*, Vol. 31 No. 3, 1966, p. 334–337

Note: Five authors, six lists of commonalities between Mesoamerica and the Mideast. No authors and no lists of any commonalities between Mesoamerica and Siberia or Asia exist because there are no commonalities between Mesoamerica and Siberia or Asia.

CHAPTER 22: Cultural Remembrance of the Asteroid

52. We have known for a long time, by the writings handed down by our forefathers, that neither I nor any who inhabit this land are natives of it, but foreigners who came here from remote parts. We also know that we were led here by a ruler, whose subjects we all were, who returned to his country, and after a long time came here again and wished to take his people away. But they had married wives and built homes, and they would neither go with him nor recognize him as their king; therefore he went back. We have ever believed that those who were of his lineage would some time come and claim this land as his, and us as his vassals. From the direction whence you came, which is where the sun rises, and from what you tell me of this great lord who sent you, we believe and think it certain that he is our natural ruler, especially since you say that for a long time he has known about us. Therefore you may feel certain we shall obey you, and shall respect you as holding the place of that great lord, and in all the land I rule, you may give what orders you wish, and they shall be obeyed and everything we have shall be put at your service. And since you are thus in your own heritage and your own house, take your ease and rest from the fatigue of the journey and the wars you have had on the way.

Rupert Furneaux, *Ancient Mysteries*, p. 160.

53. Plato's story is too long to reproduce in this text but it is readily available in other works, for example; *The Secret of Atlantis*, Otto Muck; *Atlantis: the Eighth Continent*, Charles Berlitz; *Atlantis: The Autediluvian World*, Ignatius Donnelly; *Lost Outpost of Atlantis*, Richard Wingate.

Part VI: Conclusion

CHAPTER 24: Speculation and Comment

54. Albert Einstein had a long interest in geophysical phenomena. He once wrote a paper, now little known, on why rivers meander.

55. Professor Hapgood suggests holding an earth map globe with the force line (asteroid flight path) up and down and fingers to both sides. Crustal movement force is maximum in the middle and diminishes to zero at the finger points.

56. Hundreds of feet-high tsunamis, diminishing in depth inland would destroy monumental stone buildings in their path, as would even a much smaller tsunami. An example of this is the experience of Seward, Alaska. In 1964, an underwater earthquake in the Gulf of Alaska sent a tsunami into the bay which is Seward's harbor. The wave's strength was such that it rolled a diesel locomotive engine parked at the shoreline up a slight incline for three city blocks. This was a small tsunami.

57. Overpopulation is a relative thing and depends almost solely on agriculture. In the modern United States one farmer feeds 200 people so a large population is not overpopulation. But in ancient times one farmer fed four people and a modest population in numbers was over-population. In fact, if a farmer could feed four people, six people was massive overpopulation. Overpopulation depends on the ratio of people to the food supply and not on great numbers of people. An example of this is the Vikings whose impetus to terrorize the world came from over-population.

58. Henry Rowe Schoolcraft (1793–1864) was an explorer and ethnologist who spent a lifetime living with and studying the eastern Indian tribes.

59. All religion is a product of the imagination and wholly irratio-nal. Its root is in the most primitive time of man's evolutionary progress from animal to human, perhaps mid-Homo erectus, 1 million years ago.

The First Civilization as it developed from nothing to its apex at 10,500 B.P., developed all the accoutrements of a high Stone Age civilization, monumental architecture, ships, organized government, etc., and an established religion invested with priests. By synthesizing the religions of the reemerging civilizations—which are remarkably similar—we can make suppositions as to its character. Above all it was bloodthirsty. All reemerging civilizations practiced human sacrifice, especially the Mesoamericans to an astonishing degree. This practice vividly shows the stranglehold priests had on Mesoamerican society.

> Human sacrifice quite obviously plays more definitely into the hands of the religious egotist and the dominant group than any other form of sacrifice. The reason lies in the fact that it can develop easily into a form of appeal practically identical in nature with the tyrannous constraint exercised by a man seeking power and prestige, and it thus becomes only too welcome a weapon, in a caste or class society, for those in control not to resort to its use continually.
> Paul Radin, *Primitive Religion*, p. 180

Lack of enthusiasm for the practice by the masses being sacrificed can have dire results. The success of Hernán Cortés and his handful of Spaniards in defeating the Aztec empire was due in great part to the disaffection of many subjugated Indian tribes who allied with him against the Aztecs. One of his soldiers describes a surprise visit by Mexican (Aztec) "tax collectors" to a small town:

> While this conversation was going on, some Indians from the town came in great haste to tell the Caciques who were talking to Cortés, that five Mexicans, who were Montezuma's tax gatherers, had just arrived. When they heard the news they turned pale and trembled with fear, and leaving Cortés alone they went off to receive the Mexicans, in the shortest possible time they had decked a room with flowers, and had food cooked for the Mexicans to eat, and prepared plenty of cacao, which is the best thing they have to drink.
> When these five Indians entered the town, they came to the place where we were assembled, where were the houses of the Cacique and our quarters, and approaching us with the utmost assurance and arrogance without speaking to Cortés,

or to any of us, they passed us by. Their cloaks and loincloths were richly embroidered, and their shining hair was gathered up as though tied on their heads, and each one smelled the roses that he carried, and each had a crooked staff in his hand. Their Indian servants carried fly-whisks and they were accompanied by many of the chief men of the other Totonac towns, who until they had shown them to their lodgings and brought them food of the best, never left them.

As soon as they had dined they sent to summon the fat Cacique and the other chiefs, and scolded them for entertaining us in their houses, for now they would have to speak and deal with us which would not please their lord, Montezuma; for without his permission and orders they should not have sheltered us, nor given us presents of golden jewels, and on this subject they uttered many threats against the fat Cacique and the other chiefs and ordered them at once to provide twenty Indians, men and women, to appease their gods for the wrong that had been done.

Bernal Diaz del Castillo, *The Discovery and Conquest of Mexico*, p. 90

Thus, the religion of the First Civilization and the reemerging civilizations was disingenuous, oppressive, and alienated the common people—the road to failure.

The quality of religious thought alone can do great harm to a nation. Richard Carrington uses India and China as examples in *A Million Years of Man*:

The caste system was one of the most shameful concepts in the whole history of human thought . . . largely as a result of these prejudices, Indian society became almost entirely static, a kind of gigantic octopus slowly strangling itself with its own tentacles of ignorance and superstition. The tragic result of this uneconomic and intellectually unsound system are now only too apparent among the undernourished and often hopeless millions who still make up so much of the country's population.

Pure Taoism remains an interesting example of an evolutionary cancer at the mental level—a kind of proliferation of the cells of idleness. But the fact that in its undisciplined form it led to a disastrous retardation of thought does not invalidate the value of contemplation as an aid to human awareness.

(Richard Carrington, *A Million Years of Man*, p. 204, 209)

Man failed to reduce the most barbarous aspects of religion to an acceptable level (it fully supported slavery until the end of the United States Civil War, 1865) and religion still carries on its most ancient fantasies. It would seem that evolutionary progress would be toward rational thought—and that man would eventually be physically unable to believe mindless superstitions. Hopefully, this is true, and we note that both Darwin and Sagan believe that intelligence and behavior are subject to natural selection which would lead to this result. As man's brain possess a duality—for example, working Monday through Friday building a jet aircraft engine and then spending Sunday morning listening to and believing the most ridiculous religious fantasies—we can use this fact to quantify the evolutionary development of man's brain and say "we are only half way there"—to fully rational thought. This creates optimism in that it shows man still has great intellectual potential; it creates pessimism in that it shows time may run out for man—from overpopulation and overexploitation of the earth's resources, before he is mentally capable of correcting the problems he has created. Religion brings to light another surprising fact—the old cliché "man is the only rational animal" is utterly erroneous. Man is the only irrational animal. A common mouse, squirrel, deer, or bear must be exquisitely rational to survive in the world and it focuses on survival. Only Homo sapiens, with the enlarged Neocortex for cognitive thinking, and time for reflection, can engage in running his life according to fantastic and irrational ideas. Amazingly this mental trait appeared coeval with bipedalism and shows little likelihood of abating. Despite Homo sapiens' technical prowess his brain remains true to its primitive past and packs enormous potential for irrational thought. We are only halfway down the trees.

60. Note that the Troano Codex gives a date of "8060 years ago" for the catastrophe. This plainly means from when legend was first recorded; a date we do not know. (But we can compute the recording date to 438 B.C. as follows: true date of impact 8498 B.C. Gregorian calendar, less 8,060 years is 438 B.C.) The Egyptian priest who told Solon this story of Atlantis as recorded by Plato dated the catastrophe at between

8,000 and 9,000 years before their talk (600 B.C.). Thus two legends of the Atlantic catastrophe have substantially the same date for its occurrence. And the legends—one from Egypt, the other from Central America— are half a world apart with no possible connection between them. The Camp Century Greenland ice core confirms the legends: The asteroid fell into the North Atlantic Ocean in 8500 B.C. (that is 10,500 B.P.).

61. The Maya came close to being wiped out by repeated epidemics of smallpox, influenza, yellow fever, measles, and tuberculosis, brought by Europeans and malaria and hookworm by African slaves.

> "In fact, so horrifying were the effects of European diseases upon the Maya that some authorities estimate the population of certain tribes was reduced by 75 to 90 percent in the century immediately after the conquest.
> (Charles Gallenkamp, *Maya*, p. 8)

This pattern repeated itself over the entire New World. In Peru, there were 9 million natives in 1533; 500,000 by the early 1600s; and, in Central America there were 11 million in 1519 and 1.25 million by 1625. In North America, disease often killed 95 percent of the Indians. Apart from disease European behavior decimated the Indians who were from the start regarded as inferior only fit to be slaves (in his first report to Ferdinand and Isabella, Columbus opined that the friendly Carribs would make excellent slaves). It took twenty years of intensive study by the Catholic church until Pope Julius II officially declared at the Fifth Lateran Council that the American Indians were descendants of Adam and Eve, hence were human beings and had a soul. Thus they needed to be converted to the true faith, but this did not prevent them from being made slaves. (The beautiful missions of California were in fact prison farms. The natives worked like serfs or slaves, and the monks would publicly torture the ones that were caught trying to flee to deter others from trying to escape.)

CHAPTER 25: The New Order versus the Old Order

62. The great German physicist Max Plank (1858–1947), founder of quantum mechanics is given credit for this thought.

63. One who has read the plethora of anthropological books available today all written by the Old Order can only agree with Heyerdahl. Boats do not even get passing mention. But a curious thing is starting to happen. A few of the Old Order are beginning to feel nervous about the "down through 3,000 miles of ice" theory of the populating of the Americas—at last suspecting such a journey is impossible and that it never happened—but to salvage some honor they now propose that the journey from Asia was made by boat. This would entail a voyage following the Pacific sea current far to the north along Alaska, then following the pack ice south from Alaska along 2,000 miles of glacier (no shore); and because of giant storms coming out of the Gulf of Alaska this coast is thought by some mariners to be the worst in the world in danger to ships. The west coast of Vancouver Island is called "The Graveyard of the Pacific" and it still sports the "lifesaving trail"—a path for the few shipwreck survivors to walk south to safety, now world-renowned for its majestic wilderness beauty.

Heyerdahl lists four common misconceptions about seafaring. These are: 1) a watertight hull is required for safety at sea (a raft or reed boat does just fine); 2) a large boat is safer than a small boat (a small boat handles easier); 3) hugging a coastline is safer than the open ocean (exactly the opposite is true; this is the most common misconception); 4) a ship travels the same route to a place and back (primitive navigators had to follow the wind and currents.; they could never backtrack).

And the ice. Pack ice existed far into the Gulf of Alaska and drift ice occasionally reached Hawaii (which had mountain glaciers) during the Ice Age. Pack and drift ice extended well off the coast of the Pacific Northwest down to the present United States-Canadian boundary. Thus no going near shore here in violation of Heyerdahl observation number 3. The trip from Asia would have to be nonstop requiring an advanced ship design and a very experienced crew; and of course there is no archaeological record of any such impossible journey.

We see in our mind's eye a voyage of incredible length, hardship, difficulty, and danger. Worse than any Viking voyage ever made. Hardly one for inexperienced pilgrim families going to an unknown land. The voyage exists only in the imagination of the anthropologists who have dreamed it. There are absolutely no facts that support it. This is nonscience at its worst.

CHAPTER 26: The Future

64. Excellent work has been done in this area by Professor Heather Harris of the University of Northern British Columbia, lecturer on *Late Pleistocene Environments from Northern Northwest Coast Oral History*. Below you will find an excerpt from the program that describes her talk at an anthropological conference held at Central Washington University in 1997.

> The peoples of the northern Northwest Coast area (Ts'imsian, Nisga'a, Gitxsan, Haida, Tlingit, Tahltan and others) have an oral historical record which reached back to the late Pleistocene. The stories describe the early peopling of the area after deglaciation in terms which Westerns can recognize as historical. The elders of this area tell the stories chronologically, and the very early stories clearly describe postglacial environments and events. The stories describe a treeless land which was changing rapidly. They describe sea levels much lower than present and aerially exposed land where none is now. They describe the rapid rise of sea level between 10,500 and 9500 B.P. and the effects of isostatic rebound in the inland area. The stories describe proglacial lakes, reversal of river drainages, the breaking of ice dams and other events and conditions which are likely to have prevailed before 9000 B.P.

The white man only tumbled to the fact of the Ice Ages in 1900, as a result of the efforts of Louis Agassiz but the Pacific Northwest Indians have known about it for 10,000 years since it happened! What if this oral history had become known about 1850—would it not have been scoffed at, derided, held as additional proof by the Old Order that the Indians do not know what they are talking about? The Indians' history is absolutely correct, and if it were not for the effort of one fine scholar we would not know it even existed. How many more have been ignored by the Old Order?

BIBLIOGRAPHY

An annotated copy of this book is deposited in the Library of Congress in Washington, D.C.

Alvarez, L. W. et al. "Extraterrestrial Cause for the Cretaceous–Tertiary Extinction." *Science.* June 1980, Vol. 208 No. 4448: 1095.

Allen, Oliver E. *Planet Earth Atmosphere*, Virginia: Time-Life Books, 1983.

Asimov, Isaac. *The New Intelligent Man's Guide to Science.* New York: Basic Books, Inc., 1960.

Bahn, Paul G., and Vertut, Jean. *Images of the Ice Age.* New York: Facts on File, Inc., 1988.

Bauval, Robert. *The Orion Mystery.* New York: Three Rivers Press, 1994.

Berlitz, Charles. *Atlantis: The Eight Continent*, New York: Fawcett Crest, 1984.

Berlitz, Charles. *Mysteries from Forgotten Worlds.* Garden City, N.Y.: Doubleday, 1972.

Boas, Franz. *The Mind of Primitive Man.* New York: Macmillan, 1965.

Boorstin, Daniel J. *The Discoverers.* New York: Random House, 1985.

Brunhouse, Robert L. *In Search of the Maya.* New York: Ballantine Books, 1973.

Burenhult, Goran. *The First Humans.* New York: Harper Collins, 1993.

Campbell, Joseph. *The Masks of God: Primitive Mythology.* New York: Viking Press, 1959.

Carrington, Richard. *A Million Years of Man.* New York: Mentor, 1964.

Carson, Rachel. *The Sea Around Us.* Middlesex, England: Penguin Books, 1954.

Childress, David Hatcher. *Lost Cities and Ancient Mysteries of South America.* Illinois: Adventures Unlimited Press, 1985.

Chorlton, Windsor. *Planet Earth Ice Ages.* Virginia: Time-Life Books, 1983.

Clark, Grahame. *World Prehistory.* London: Cambridge University Press, 1961.

Clark, Ronald W. *The Survival of Charles Darwin*. New York Random House, 1984.

Coe, M., Snow, D., and Benson, E. *Atlas of Ancient America*. New York: Facts on File, Inc., 1986.

Coe, Michael D. *The Maya*. New York: Frederick A. Praeger, 1966.

Darwin, Charles. *The Descent of Man*. New York Random House, 1871.

Darwin, Charles. *The Expression of the Emotions in Man and Animals*. Chicago: University of Chicago Press,1965.

Darwin, Charles. *The Origin of Species*. New York: Random House, 1859.

DeCamp, L. Sprague. *The Ancient Engineers*. New York: Ballantine Books, Inc., 1960.

Decker, Robert, and Decker, Barbara B.. *Mountains of Fire*. Cambridge: Cambridge University Press, 1991.

del Castillo, Bernal Diaz. *The Discovery and Conquest of Mexico*. New York: Farrar, Straus and Cudahay, 1956.

de Santillana, Giorgio, and von Dechend, Hertha. *Hamlet's Mill*. Boston: David R. Godine, 1977.

Desonie, Dana. *Cosmic Collisions*. New York. Henry Holt, 1966.

Dillehay, Tom D. "A Late Ice-Age Settlement in Southern Chile." *Scientific American*, Oct. 1984.

Donnelly, Ignatius. *Atlantis: The Antediluvian World*. New York: Dover Publications, Inc., 1976.

Dorfman Andrea. "New Ways to the New World." *Time Magazine*, 17 April 2000.

Dyson, James L. *The World of Ice*. New York: Alfred A. Knopf, 1962.

Edey, M. A., and Johanson, D. C.. *Blueprints*, New York: Penguin Books, 1989.

Edwards, I. E. S. *The Pyramids of Egypt*. New York: Penguin Books, Ltd., rev. ed., 1961.

Fell, Barry. *America B.C.*. New York: Simon & Schuster, Inc., 1976.

Fell, Barry. *Bronze Age America*. New York: Ruggles DeLatour, Inc., 1982.

Fell, Barry. *Saga America*. New York: Times Books, 1983.

Frankfort, Henri. *The Birth of Civilization in the Near East*. New York: Doubleday, 1956.

Frazer, Sir James George. *The Golden Bough*. New York: Criterion Books, 1890.

Furneaux, Rupert. *Ancient Mysteries*. New York: McGraw-Hill, 1977.

Gallenkamp, Charles. *Maya*. New York: David McKay Co., 1976.

Guthrie, Dale R., and Guthrie Mary L. "On the Mammoth's Dusty Trail." *Natural History*, July 1990: 34.

Hancock, Graham. *Fingerprints of the Gods*. New York: Crown Trade Paperbacks, 1995.

Hancock, Graham. *The Message of the Sphinx*. New York: Three Rivers Press, 1996.

Hapgood, Charles, H. *Earth's Shifting Crust*. New York: Pantheon Books, Inc., 1958.

Hapgood, Charles H. *Maps of the Ancient Sea Kings*. Illinois: Adventures Unlimited Press, 1966.

Hawkins, Gerald S. *Stonehenge Decoded*. Garden City, New York: Doubleday, 1965.

Heyerdahl, Thor. *Aku Aku*. New York: Rand McNally, 1958.

Heyerdahal, Thor. *Early Man and the Ocean*. Garden City, New York: Doubleday, 1979.

Heyerdahl, Thor. *Kon-Tiki*. New York: Rand McNally, 1950.

Heyerdahl, Thor. *The Ra Expeditions*. Garden City, New York: Doubleday, 1971.

Heyerdahl, Thor. *The Tigris Expedition*. Garden City, New York: Doubleday, 1981.

Hopkins, D. M. *Bering Land Bridge*. California: Stanford University Press, 1967.

Howells, William. *Back of History*. New York: Doubleday, rev. ed., 1963.

Hutchson, Robert. *The Search for Our Beginning*, Oxford: Oxford University Press, 1983.

Huxley, Thomas H. *On the Origin of Species*. Ann Arbor: University of Michigan Press, 1863.

Irwin, Constance. *Fair Gods and Stone Faces*. New York: St. Martin's Press, 1963.

James, Preston. *Geography of Man*. Waltham, Massachusetts: Blaisdell Publishing Co., 3rd ed., 1949.

Jolly, C. J., and Plog, F.. *Physical Anthropology and Archaeology*. New York: Alfred A. Knopf, Inc., 1976.

Kendrew, W. G. *The Climates of the Continents*. Oxford: Clarendon Press, 1922.

Kluckhohn, Clyde. *Mirror for Man*. Greenwich, Connecticut: Fawcett Publications, 1970.

Kuhn, Herbert. *On the Track of Prehistoric Man*. New York: Random House, 1955.

Leakey, Richard. *The Origin of Humankind*. New York: Basic Books, 1994.

Lister, Adrian, and Bahn, Paul. *Mammoths*. London: Boxtree, 1995.

Luce, J. V. *Lost Atlantic*. New York: McGraw-Hill, 1969.

"Mammoth Trumpet," Center for the Study of the First Americans, Oregon State University, Corvallis, Oregon: 1993, Vol. 8, No. 3.

"Mammoth Trumpet," Center for the Study of the First Americans, Oregon State University, Corvallis, Oregon: 1993, Vol. 9, No. 1.

"Mammoth Trumpet," Center for the Study of the First Americans, Oregon State University, Corvallis, Oregon: 2000, Vol. 15, No. 2.

Marble, Dr. Samuel D. *Before Columbus*. New Jersey: A.S. Barnes and Co., Inc., 1980.

Mather, John C. *The Very First Light*. New York: Harper Collins, 1996.

Melson, Dr. William. *Planet Earth Volcano*. Virginia: Time-Life Books, 1983.

Menzel, Donald H. *Astronomy*. New York: Random House, 1970.

Mertz, Barbara. *Temples, Tombs and Hieroglyphs*. New York: Dodd, Mead & Company, rev. ed., 1964.

Mote, F. W. *The Travels of Marco Polo*. New York: Dell, 1961.

Montagu, Ashley. *Man: First Two Million Years*. New York: Dell, 1957.

Muck, Otto. *The Secret of Atlantis*. London: Wm. Collins, Sons & Co., 1978.

Murchie, Guy. *The World Aloft*. New York: Bantam, 1960.

National Geographic Society. *Into the Unknown*. Washington D.C.: National Geographic Society, 1987.

Pielov, E. C. *After the Ice Age*. Chicago: University of Chicago Press, 1991.

Pleiffer, John E. *The Creative Explosion*. New York: Cornell University Press, 1982.

Powell, T. G. E. *Prehistoric Art*. London: Thames and Hudson Ltd, 1966.

Radin, Paul. *Primitive Man as Philosopher*. New York: Dover Publications, 1927.

Radin, Paul. *Primitive Religion*. New York: Dover Publications, 1937.

Radin, Paul. *The Story of the American Indian*. New York: Liveright Publishing Corp., 1927.

Recinos, A., Goetz, D., and Morley, S.. *Popol Vuh*, Norman, Oklahoma: University of Oklahoma Press, 1950.

Romer, Alfred Sherwood. *Man and the Vertebrates*, Illinois: University of Chicago Press, 1933.

Rowe, J. "Diffusionism and Archaeology," *American Antiquity*. 1966, Vol. 31 No. 3.

Sagan, Carl. *Cosmos*. New York: Random House, 1980.

Sagan, Carl. *The Dragons of Eden*. New York: Random House, 1977.

Sawtell, Ruth Otis, and Treat, Ida. *Primitive Hearths in the Pyrenees*. New York: D. Appleton, 1927.

Schoolcraft, Henry Rowe. *Archives of Aboriginal Knowledge*. 1860.

Shapley, H., Rapport, S., and Wright, H. *The New Treasury of Science*, New York: Harper & Row, 1965.

Silverberg, Robert. *Lost Cities and Vanished Civilizations*. New York: Bantam Pathfinder, 1962.

Smith, Gary. "Secrets of the Mummies," *Discover Magazine*, October 1986: 72.

Spence, Lewis. *The History of Atlantis*. United States: University Books, 1968.

Spindler, Konrad. *The Man in the Ice*. New York: Crown Trade Paperbacks, 1994.

Strong, Emory. *Stone Age in the Great Basin*. Portland, Oregon: Binfords & Mort, 1969.

Swift, Jeremy. *The Sahara.* Amsterdam, Time-Life Books, 1975.

Tompkins, Peter. *Mysteries of the Mexican Pyramids.* New York: Harper & Row, 1976.

Tompkins, Peter. *Secrets of the Great Pyramid.* New York: Harper & Row, 1971.

Vallentine, H. R. *Water in the Service of Man.* Baltimore: Penguin Books, Inc. 1967.

Van Sertima, Ivan. *They Came before Columbus.* New York: Random House, 1976.

Verrill, A. Hyatt. *The American Indian.* New York: The New Home Library, 1927.

von Koenigswald, G. H. R. *Meeting Prehistoric Man.* New York: Harper & Brothers, 1956.

Wendt, Herbert. *In Search of Adam.* Boston: Houghton Mifflin, 1956.

Wenke, Robert J. *Patterns in Prehistory.* Oxford: Oxford University Press, 1980.

West, John Anthony. *Serpent in The Sky.* Wheaton, Illinois: Quest Books, 1993.

Williams, M., Dunkerley, D., DeDecker, P., Kershaw, A., and Stokes, T. *Quaternary Environments.* New York: Chapman and Hall, Inc., 1993.

Willis, Delta. *The Hominid Gang.* London: Penguin Books, 1989.

Wingate, Richard. *Lost Outpost of Atlantis.* New York: Everest House, 1980.

Woodbury, David O. *The Great White Mantle.* New York: Viking Press, 1962.

Woodhead, Henry. *Time Frame The Age of God Kings.* Virginia: Time-Life Books, 1988.

Zink, Dr. David. *The Stones of Atlantis.* New York: Prentice Hall, rev. ed., 1978.

GENERAL REFERENCE BOOKS

Encyclopedia Britannica, 15th Ed., Macro, s.v. Amazon River, p. 652, 1980.

Encyclopedia Britannica, 15th Ed., Micro, s.v. American Indian Geographical Race, p. 306, 1980.

Encyclopedia Britannica, 15th Ed., Macro, s.v. Antarctica, p. 961, 1980.

Encyclopedia Britannica, 15th Ed., Macro, s.v. Populations, Human, 1980.

Encyclopedia Britannica, 15th Ed., Macro, s.v. Races of Mankind, p.353, 1980.

Encyclopedia Britannica, 15th Ed., Macro, s.v. Cretaceous Period, p. 246, 1980.

Encyclopedia Britannica, 15th Ed., Macro, s.v. Earth Geological History of, p. 8, 1980.

Encyclopedia Britannica, 15th Ed., Macro, s.v. Embryology, p. 741, 1980.

Encyclopedia Britannica, 15th Ed., Macro, s.v. Geological Time Scale, p. 1065, 1980.

Encyclopedia Britannica, 15th Ed., Macro, s.v. Mesozoic Era, p. 1013. 1980.

Encyclopedia Britannica, 15th Ed., Macro, s.v. Siberian Cultures, p. 725, 1980.

Encyclopedia Britannica, 15th Ed., Micro, s.v. Siberian Cultures, p. 179, 1980.

Encyclopedia Britannica, 15th Ed., Macro, s.v. Lapter Sea, p. 681. 1980.

Encyclopedia Britannica, 15th Ed., Macro, s.v. Pest Control, p. 145, 1980.

Encyclopedia Britannica, 15th Ed., Macro, s.v. Radiation Biological Effects of, 378 – 391, 1980.

Encyclopedia Britannica, 15th Ed., Macro, s.v. Elements Geochemical Distribution of, 1980.

Encyclopedia Britannica, 15th Ed., Macro, s.v. Van Allen Radiation Belts, 1980.

Encyclopedia Britannica, 15th Ed., Macro, s.v. Radiation Injury, 1980.

Encyclopedia Britannica, 15th Ed., Micro s.v. Radiation Belt, Inner-Outer, p. 375, 1980.

Encyclopedia Britannica, 15th Ed., Macro, s.v. Calendar, p. 595, 1980.

Encyclopedia Britannica, 15th Ed., Macro, s.v. Radio Sources, Astronomical, p. 467, 1980.

Encyclopedia Britannica, 15th Ed., Macro, s.v. Universe, Origin and Evolution of, p. 1007, 1980.

Encyclopedia Britannica, 15th Ed., Macro, s.v. Agassiz, Louis, p. 289, 1980.

Encyclopedia Britannica, 15th Ed., Micro, s.v. Dinosaur, p. 555, 1980.

Encyclopedia Britannica, 15th Ed., Micro, s.v. Coelacanth, P. 1038, 1980.

Encyclopedia Britannica, 15th Ed., Micro, s.v. Scopes Trial, p. 988, 1980.

Encyclopedia Britannica, 15th Ed., Macro, s.v. Radiation Effects on Matter, p. 399, 1980.

Encyclopedia Britannica, 15th Ed., Micro, s.v. Cubit, p. 279, 1980.

Encyclopedia Britannica, 15th Ed., Micro, s.v. Bison, p. 47, 1980.

Hubble, Edwin, on Big Bang Theory, 1
Hudson Bay, creation of, 16
human artifacts. *See* artifacts, human
human instincts, 30
hunter-gatherer people, 34–37, 41, 46–47
hydrospheric currents, 7–8

Icarus asteroid, 85
Ice Age
    end of, 15–18, 98–100, 118, 166, 176–78
    evolution of, 3, 5–8, 10, 12–14, 22–24
    mammals of, 36–37, 40–41, 66–67, 109
icebergs, 21
ice cores
    Antarctic, 104
    Greenland, 101, 103, 177
Ice Free Corridor, theory refuted, 79, 81
Iceman, discovery of, 129–30
ice sheets
    evolution of, 6–8, 11, 16–17, 44, 79
    melting of, 15, 18, 123, 176–78
impact craters
    on the earth, 83–86
    on the moon, 82–83
Imperial mammoth, 110
Indus Valley
    maritime activity in, 56, 133
    Mesozoic era, effect on, 25
    migration of man to, 43, 71, 126
    religious practices, 144
interglacial periods, 67, 190
iridium, 84, 202
irrigation systems, 63–65
isostatic rise, 17

Johanson, Donald, on Lucy, 33

katabatic winds, 10, 19
3 Kelvin universal blackbody, 1
Krakatoa volcano, 98–100, 201

Lake Nyos, Cameroon, 95
land bridges, 9–10
language development, 137–38
Laurentide ice sheet, 7, 44, 79
Leakey, Richard
    on evolution of man, 29–30
    on Turkana boy, 33–34

John Cogan

Pacific Ocean, 105
   See also oceans
Paleozoic era, 3, 25
particulate hard radiation, 119
Pelee, Mount, 94–95, 150, 201
Penzais, Arno Allan, on thermal radiation, 1
permafrost, 7, 13–14, 20, 110–13
phenomena
   of Antarctica and Greenland, 51, 54
   of asteroid impact, 101–3
   of Ice Age, 12–14, 19
Pielov, E.C., on extinction of mammals, 118
Piggott cores, 105, 189
Pikimachay Cave, Peru, 48
Piri Reis map, 50–54
planetary orbits, 82
Plato, on Atlantis, 150–51, 155–56
Pleistocene epoch, 3, 66, 116–17, 165
polar regions, occupancy of, 21
population, human, 69, 167, 170–71
Precambrian period, 2, 4
primates, evolution of, 28–32
primitive man. *See* Homo Erectus; Homo sapiens, thinking man
Procounsul, 192
proglacial lakes, 16
pumice stone, 99–100
pyramids, 126, 135–37, 170, 203
pyroclastic flow, 94

Quaternary period, 3

radiation, 118–21
rainfall, 22, 96–97
red shift, 1
reed boats, 132–33
religions, 142–43, 171–72, 206–9

Sacsay Luaman, 61–62
Sahara
   asteroid impact, effect on, 128–29
   geography of, 12, 13, 22, 66–68
   human artifacts of, 195
   See also North Africa
savannas, in Amazon Basin, 73
Schoolcraft, Henry Rowe
   on American Indians, 171
   background of, 206
sea cores, 105

Tyrannosaurus Rex, 26
See also dinosaurs

ultraviolet electromagnetic radiation, 118–20
undersea archeology, 62–63, 169, 185
United States. *See* New World; North America

Van Allen radiation belts, 120–21
volcanoes, 90–91, 93–96, 98–100, 201

Walker, Alan, on Turkana boy, 33–34
Wallace, Alfred Russell, on mammal extinction, 117
water transport
    See maritime activities
weather patterns, 22, 23, 44–46, 128–29
Wegener, Alfred, geophysicist, on continental drift, 5
Wenke, Robert, on architecture and religious traditions, 70
Whipple, Fred, on supernova theory, 2
Wilson, Robert W., on thermal radiation, 1
winds, 11, 13, 22–23, 98–99
    See also weather patterns
Wingate, Richard, on monumental structures, 62
Wooley, Sir Leonard, on Sumerian flood legend, 148
woolly mammoths, 109–15, 164–65

ziggurats, 136
Zoser step pyramid, 136

ORDER FORM

THE NEW ORDER OF MAN'S HISTORY

To order copies of *The New Order of Man's History*, please complete the information below. (Feel free to duplicate this form.)

I would like to order _____ copies of *The New Order of Man's History* at $20.00 per copy (plus postage and handling).

$_____ TOTAL COST OF BOOKS ($xx.00 per copy)

$_____ SALES TAX
Washington residents add 8.8% (or $x.xx per book)

$_____ SHIPPING AND HANDLING
$2.00 for first book, $1.00 for each additional book (sent to same address)

$_____ **TOTAL AMOUNT ENCLOSED**

ORDERED BY:

Name_____

Address_____

City/State/Zip_____

Phone (_____)_____

E-mail_____

SHIP TO: (if different from above)

Ordered by_____

Name_____

Address_____

City/State/Zip_____

Phone (_____)_____

E-mail_____

Mail a copy of this form and a check to:
New Order Press
P.O. Box 2454
Woodinville, WA 98072-9998